WONDERFUL WORLD OF
WORDERS

GUILDHALL PRESS

Published in September 2007

Guildhall Press
Unit 15
Ráth Mór Business Park
Bligh's Lane
Derry BT48 0LZ
T: (028) 7136 4413 F: (028) 7137 2949
info@ghpress.com www.ghpress.com

Typesetting: Joe McAllister
Editors: Paul Hippsley and Jenni Doherty
Cover design: Kevin Hippsley

A copy of the British Library Cataloguing-in-Publication data is
available from the British Library.

The authors assert their moral rights in this work in accordance with the
Copyright, Designs and Patents Act 1998.

Copyright © Authors / Guildhall Press
ISBN 978 1 906271 04 6

We gratefully acknowledge the financial support of the Arts Council of
Northern Ireland under its Multi-Annual Lottery Programme.

Acknowledgements

I'd like to thank Paul, Joe, Kevin, Declan and Aaron of Guildhall Press for all their hard work, friendship and humour plus Damian Smyth and the Arts Council of Northern Ireland for supporting and funding this project. Thanks also to writer Sean O'Reilly for his most inspiring foreword and to all the online writing communities where words and relationships have been created and thrive to do so.

To all the wonderful contributors from across the world, especially those from the former BBC Get Writing website who have remained passionate, enthusiastic and supportive for the last four years – long may our friendships and scribblings continue.

I would also like to acknowledge the kindness of the authors who contributed to our associated charity, Action With Effect.

I'd like to further acknowledge all the online writers that are no longer with us, especially Peter Rafferty (aka Hackenbush from the MoreWriting website whose daughter Amy has some Worders included herein) and DottyFix from Get Writing and the Writers' Dock sites for being a big part of these communities, helping and befriending many. May their own words and memory live on.

Special thanks due also to: my parents, my siblings and their children; to Michael and Shorty (my wee dog who likes sitting on books rather than reading them); and to my poetic partners in crime, The Poetry Chicks: Pamela Brown and Abby Oliveira, for all their patience, encouragement, laughter and friendship. It's been a wonderful experience!

Action With Effect
Charity Recipients

Action With Effect (AWE) wishes to sincerely thank Guildhall Press for their ongoing support and all those Worders authors who have generously donated their fees for this publication to the charity's work in India.

AWE is an Irish-based Third World registered charity (Number XR 88946) that has been involved with relieving the plight of destitute lepers, homeless street children and orphans in India since its formation in 2005. The charity's coordinator is Eamon Melaugh, a native of Derry, who carried out this work in India for many years on a personal basis before he founded the charity. AWE provides funding to an Indian registered Christian charity, Eco-Adventreks & Welfare Society. Together they have built: nine schools for destitute "Untouchable" children; fifty houses for homeless lepers; and an orphanage for girls and boys. Currently they are raising funds to build a hospice in the Hardwar region, north of Delhi.

Information on the charity's aims and work can be found on www.actionwitheffect.com. Donations to: **Action With Effect,** 38 Bishop Street, Derry, N Ireland, BT48 6UX. Tel: (028) 7136 4029. Email: info@actionwitheffect.com

Foreword

The online writing group or community offers the contemporary writer radical opportunities for sharing and publishing their work. Any new literary medium will create its own unique forms and the Worder is one of them.

The editor of this collection, Jenni Doherty, has gathered some of the best examples of this new form from across the world. Like any good story or anecdote told in passing, the Worder seems to be an attempt at capturing the significance of the moment. Perhaps it has links with the haiku and what Joyce called 'epiphany' – the shout in the street, the overheard conversation, the tap on the window late at night, and even the joke.

Worders are thresholds where the self suddenly understands where it stands in the world. They aspire to being instantaneous as a text message but can be thought about again and again as small parables of human life. The luminous moment must fade . . . but the memory remains and is transformed into language by these writers co-operating across global boundaries.

Here, then, is a stimulating and often moving collection of new writing born from the fusion of today's technology with the human experience of the vastness of every passing moment.

Sean O'Reilly
Derry, 2007

Sean O'Reilly is the author of: *Curfew and Other Stories* (2000), *Love and Sleep* (2002), *The Swing of Things* (2004) and *Watermark* (2005).

In loving memory of Nana and Julie

Introduction

Writing is an isolated pastime. For many writers, feedback and discussion are crucial in honing the craft and skills needed to shape their work into something that is original and interesting. Joining a local writing group isn't always an option, as people work long hours, have less free time, live in remote areas or the opportunities are non-existent.

I worked full time. I didn't know of any local writing groups – or of other writers in my area. I didn't want to do an evening course plus it wouldn't suit as I was at my best – writing-wise – in the wee small hours. So I wrote alone, in secret and didn't show my work to anyone.

Then, in April 2004, I came across an online writing community called BBC Get Writing (GW). I was curious and, yes, wanted to "get writing" again. It had been twelve years since I'd penned any poetry or prose. I had lots of non-fiction work, comment pieces, reviews and snapshots of words, but nothing truly creative. I was watching too much chewing-gum telly, reading too many bubblegum books but not getting enough literary stimulation. Plus I was bored and didn't sleep much.

And there began my introduction – and addiction – to online-writing communities: the desire to write and learn from others, the need to seek out new styles and voices, cultures and attitudes, the chance to receive feedback and criticism. It was a whole new world and one I grasped with anticipated enthusiasm. Here I found instantaneous exposure, live discussion, debate and the opportunity to workshop, plus meet writers from all over the world, many of whom have now become good friends.

But the BBC decided to close down their site in March 2005. This wonderful community of writers was going to be frozen in time with no more live input or communication. Strong bonds had been formed and, as any solid community would, members pulled together, fought an ambitious (yet unsuccessful) campaign and never lost hope. Two members, themselves writers, Gordon Brooks (aka Cadwallon) and Stephen Gritton (aka Sonny), went on to create their own writing sites – MoreWriting (MW) at www.morewriting.co.uk and Writers' Dock (WD) at www.writersdock.org – where many of us are now based and actively writing.

On these two sites, all types of writing have been created and one such discipline included micro-stories, collectively called Worders: stories that varied from 60 to 100 to 250 words on specific titles. The original idea of gathering all these gems together for publication was first suggested to me by Damian and Lynda Kenny (aka Lyndabk) back in 2005 after many of us were first introduced to the Worder style by Ali Froud (aka Spiderbaby) on the GW site.

Receiving immediate feedback and comment online has been crucial to many of the writers in this collection. Where else could writers so easily discuss and explain their work with other writers – all readers themselves? Where else but online could you find such a vibrant gathering, showcasing a singular, thrilling and hugely diverse community of writers from throughout the world? And the result of this co-operative online work is the contents of this book.

The *Wonderful World of Worders* (WWW) is a representation of some of the best of the creative fiction first posted in the various Worder groups on these sites: the 60-Word Fiction Group (MW); the 60/100 Worder Group (GW); Wee Stories Group (MW); and the Small But Perfectly Formed Group (WD). All stories have been written between 2004 and 2007. WWW also includes invited pieces by writers from www.editred.com, www.myspace.com and some sole writers by email.

This discovery and wealth of talent, and vigorous gathering and sorting of material, finally led to this collection – a collection like no other – and bravely endorsed by our publishers, Guildhall Press, themselves at the cutting edge of innovative publishing. Guildhall Press was willing to take on this unique project and to publish and publicise new and unknown writers from around the world, a task that many mainstream publishers would never even consider.

Publishers can be quite conservative and averse to risk taking. They often, therefore, tend to play safe by filtering out new ideas which determines (and limits to some degree) what the public actually gets to read and buy. We, as readers, may think we are being offered a wide choice of topics and writers, but we aren't. Online writing breaks that cycle and so it is encouraging in this instance that both media can combine and that the variety of topics and diversity of writers first digitally "published" on the internet can successfully transfer to the printed page.

Anthologies can appear too clean, ordered and contemporary. Yet in this collection, rules are broken, new words are formed, adventurous styles are created, taboo subjects are addressed and sometimes written in a very bold and blunt way, all with something to say and very much the authors' own work. This is the real beauty of this collection.

Here are writers – some already published, some first timers – who all have personal stories they needed to express in fiction. For some, English has not been their first language therefore some Worders have been specifically written or translated into English for this collection. The seventy-two authors involved range from eight years of age to middle age and represent twenty-seven countries including Ireland, the UK, France, Bulgaria, Russia, America, Zimbabwe, Kuwait, India, Australia and Kenya.

Here are stories, alive with originality, craft, emotion and ideas. These instant micro-pieces range from contemporary modern-day issues to horror, from science fiction to romance, humour to grief, religion to satire, philosophy to surrealism, and some are just plain wacky! Diverse indeed, but all genres and styles that we have come to expect from full novels. Individually, the Worders may have little or no access or outlet to the reading public, no other way of being heard or read. But – as a complete package – they work brilliantly together.

In this fast-moving age of juggling work and family life, commuting and queuing, overtime competing with quality time, it has become harder for people to find extended opportunities to relax and read. These Worders can be accessed in those spare moments between appointments and business meetings, on the train to work, on a tea break, at the doctor's or hairdresser's etc – all places where we can either choose to waste our time or put it to better use. By reading. Each distinct thread will please existing fans of fiction and inspire newcomers. The audience can pick and mix their topics, their genres, their writing styles and their reading times. Ideal for adults on the go and those with short concentration spans, whereby Worders may well become the preferred literature choice of tomorrow.

This is a wild, invigorating, exciting extravaganza of assorted literary works from all walks of life and corners of the world. Fresh, fast and fun, this collection proves we can communicate at anytime, any place and anywhere. It also proves that fiction continues to be a stimulating, challenging, boundary-breaking genre with many dimensions still to be explored. The *Wonderful World of Worders* is just one of those exciting dimensions that will reach readers that other writing cannot reach. Guildhall Press has given these hidden stories a life of their own and for that, I am truly grateful.

We are no longer isolated but brought together by word and language, by idea and passion both in print and online. Friendships have been made and stories have been shared. It has been a wonderful experience for all involved. Long live the short story in this wonderful world of words. So, let this journey – your journey – to another place begin and never cease.

Ina grá, Jenni Doherty
Derry, August 2007
www.myspace.com/wonderfulworldofworders

Contents

An Inspiring Worder
Written by our youngest contributor,
Saoirse Doherty, when aged eight

My World   *Saoirse Doherty*

I am as cool as 50 Cent. I am as strong and as brave
as a Roman soldier. I am as gentle as a small teddy, as
fast as a Ferrari speeding on the highway, as slow as a
lazy turtle, as happy as the richest kid in the universe.
I am as silly as Homer Simpson when he goes to the
pub, as good as gold in a treasure chest, as funny as a
clown with a big red nose.

I come into this unusual place. There is a beautiful
sunset. There is no hate.

This is an amazing world.

---

*Saoirse, now aged nine years, is a keen footballer and avid
Simpsons' fan. He goes to school in Derry and lives with his
mum, Olivia, spending most of his weekends in Donegal
with his grandparents. He loves animals, sports and com-
puters and wants to be either a professional footballer or a
singer when he grows up. This is his first time in print.*

Welcome to the
WONDERFUL WORLD OF
WORDERS

A Tap at the Window   *Jenni Doherty*

Two weeks before Christmas, we started counting trees.

Crouched in the back of Dad's car, we silently tip-tapped the window, excited little nine-year-old fingerprints veined like butterflies' wings. The mystic, silvery-blue ocean held only the shimmering reflection of frosty stars as we sped along, stunned by the rush of sparkling jewels from strangers' darkened front rooms; majestic evergreens, bedecked like emperors, or little crooked shrubs knobbled with lights, bright and sticky like boiled sweets. Chimney-smoke snatches on the smudge of dusk made us yearn for Santa on a garland of dreams.

Oh, how I loved coming home!

A Tap at the Window   *Neil Outram*

The grandfather clock chimed for midnight. Christmas Day. Mark was looking out to the snow tumbling down like luminous rain when there was a tap at the window behind him. It was a man dressed as Santa.

'Go away or I'll throw hot coffee in your face!' shouted Mark.

'Oh, would you? That'd be a grand treat in these harsh conditions.'

'What? No. I'll throw cold water in your face, then. Sod off!'

And so it was that Mark never received any presents that Christmas – or any Christmas – because he was found dead the next morning, mown down by reindeer.

A Tap at the Window   *Lynda Kenny*

She awoke in abject terror, clutching the blanket to her chin, afraid to move. Her eyes, wide-open and staring, darted round the room, trying to make sense of the— There it was again! A faint tapping at the window. Her blood turned to ice water as she broke into a cold sweat. Her breathing became laboured and she started to wheeze as a full-blown asthma attack struck. Bravely extending one frail arm to her nightstand in search of her inhaler . . . It came again, sharper and more insistent. Her arm fell back and her eyes bulged as her breathing stopped.

A Tap at the Window   *Mark Buchanan*

The seven-mile descent into the cold, dark depths of the abyss went smoothly without the slightest hint of a malfunction. The light glimmered down to pitchy blackness and the temperature dropped to near freezing; but we were rewarded by the light shows of dancing bioluminescent marine life.

The horrible, creaking groans from the ballast tanks compressing under the enormous pressure didn't worry us much. Only when, with a soft thud, we reached bottom did our problems begin; we heard a tap at the window and watched in horror as a thin crack slowly grew from one side to the other.

A Tap at the Window   *Darren Wheatley*

She was late. Again. I drummed my fingers on the table and tried to look like I had better things to do. I didn't. The office had closed two weeks ago, something about "moving leaner and fitter into the months ahead". Some old bull-shine anyway. I'd not told her yet. Had to soon, though; there was no way I could keep up the pretence.

A short rap on glass and she was there, outside, arms full of shopping, big smile on her beautiful face. She loved me, trusted me, depended on me. What the hell! I'd tell her after Christmas.

A Tap at the Window   *Jill Paiton*

The dish of king prawns and ginger shallots arrived with efficient style and minimum flourish. He thought to himself, *I deserve this; I've earned this promotion to Managing Director.* True, he had made sacrifices, and some had cost him his family. Still, that was all in the past. Hey, they didn't know of this new life. The maintenance cheques were never paid. He was just about to place the succulent prawn morsel into his mouth when a tap at the restaurant window caused him to freeze in motion. Standing outside the five-star restaurant were his ex-wife and three kids.

A Tap at the Window   *Estelle Kirk*

Between the rusty bars and the thick, grey grime of the window were three inches of cobweb, full of dead flies. The hostage sat there shivering and soiled, her legs stiff with being tied up for so long. She reached through the bars for one last tap at the window.

Rashid strolled along the street, past the old factory windows, his Walkman turned up loud. He loved American rock music, although he hated Americans. He saw his uncle turn the corner and pulled the Walkman out of sight just in time, but just too late to hear the faint knocking.

A Tap at the Window   *Calvin Lord*

Ahmed heard the tap, short and insistent, and ran into the dust and sweat outside. He stood on tiptoes, straining over the shoulders of the fruit seller, who was tense and quiet like the rest of the crowd. They had gathered to gawp at the beheaded orange-suited mannequin, spread-eagled in awkward pose on the stinking refuse of the market street, thick with a fog of flies. The low wail of the muezzin's call cut through the silence from on high.

'The knife was too short and blunt,' Ahmed reflected.

He turned and walked up the hill to prayer.

A Token Gesture   *Liz Gallagher*

It started with a kiss. Pernods line the counter. Her belt is tight. Brand-new curls rest on her forehead. She likes how they spring back into place. Persistence. One consolation is to return home on a tractor beneath the stars. He promises to grip her tight. She thinks about pointlessness. A sharp stone rolls about inside her shoe. Trees cast shadows. The wheels squeal to a stop. He leaves the engine running. They descend. He returns her Hot Chocolate tape. The cover is newly cracked. She bends forward, rests a hand on his shoulder, and shakes out the stone.

A Token Gesture   *Estelle Kirk*

In the morning, she stretched and rubbed her eyes. Everything was going to be perfect! But where were her oyster-silk, kitten-heeled shoes? Tiny scraps of pale fabric were scattered on the carpet and her faithful dog hid quietly under the bed.

She helter-skeltered down the stairs to find her Mum bent over the kitchen table, sewing madly. She had been up for hours, painstakingly trying to repair the wedding shoes. To hide the patched and pieced-together silk, she had embroidered them with scrolls and roses, and hidden on the side were tiny stitches that said "we love you".

Alien   *Darren Wheatley*

It used to be fun around here. You could run a few landing lights, scare the locals, maybe even get your photo on the front of Ripley's. But since everybody's on something these days, you just get passed off as a hallucination. Even the cow mutilations fail to raise eyebrows. Looking like nothing on earth sure ain't what it was!

Alien *Jill Paiton*

Her emotions raced, desperately searching out a template for such an experience. A few procedures on, she became wary of emotion, on automatic pilot, clinical, detached, and removed from present-day life. Until the twelfth week of Nisan, when she read on the intergalactic language decoder: 'Congratulations, Ms Jones. You have four beautiful Zandorian embryos.'

Emotions were no longer alien.

Alien *Karen Jones*

The tests revealed the disturbing truth: its physiology was remarkably similar to their own. It would be kinder to kill it quickly and grasp science's Holy Grail: an alien autopsy. The human's eyes leaked liquid fear, as though it knew what they were thinking. But that was ridiculous: its body might be like theirs, but its intellect was vastly inferior.

Alien *Elizabeth Madden*

Hidden from view, she looked but was unseen. She walked abroad, absorbing the world, felt safe within her carapace of darkness. But now, all eyes are upon her. Knowing glances. Looks of hate, of suspicion, of fear. They want to tear away her veil. Send her back whence she came. She is an alien, a dangerous foreigner who threatens them all.

Almost There *Shirley Bunyan*

Small and afraid, she stared out from the orphanage window.

'Some day, someone will love me.'

She believed this with all her heart, nurturing the tiny flame that flickered deep inside.

Years passed. The flame warmed and grew, firing her beauty,

filling her with hope. She went into the world and watched it fall at her feet. They clawed and clamoured for her charms. She captured and was imprisoned; conquered and was enslaved.

The flame grew weak. Small and afraid, she stared out from the penthouse window.

'Someday, someone will love me.'

There were times she was almost there.

Almost There   *Perry Gretton*

She's sitting by the window in the grey autumn light when I arrive.

'Hello, Mum.'

She turns to look at me. A suspicious flicker of recognition and then, 'Who are you? What do you want?'

'I'm Andrew, Mum. Your son, remember?'

'Don't be daft. Andy's at school. Are you his teacher?'

I retreat into the kitchen and put the kettle on. She calls out to me. 'Don't forget, I'm down to one sugar now, Andrew.'

'I've not forgotten.' I take the tea in to her and sit down. She gives me an encouraging smile.

'Andy will be home from school soon.'

Almost There   *Teresa Stenson*

I know I'm the one she never really wanted. I'm the one she chose not to choose. Sometimes she thinks of me and we meet, and I watch her, walking ahead until she turns to me with the look in her eye like she might . . . We don't.

I'm the one she says goodbye to. She, aware of her lips; me, trying not to let my eyes look like they're in love with her. She knows if we were together, the house would be big. Then she's gone, back to him, until she needs our next almost.

Almost There

Sam Robinson

Angus and Fiona met Sandy on a misty mountainside.

'Can I join you?' Sandy asked.

They chatted during the struggle to the summit where, despite thick cloud, they wanted him to take their photo, but somehow he'd vanished. That evening, Fiona spotted Sandy's picture in the paper with a report that he'd died on active service in Basra the week before. She phoned his parents in Manchester.

'I received his last letter today,' his mother said. 'His final words were, "I'll be home on leave next week. I want to climb Ben Nevis if it's the last thing I do."'

Almost There

Lynda Kenny

The boy with the pale grey eyes stared off into the distance. The mountain range seemed small and easy to climb from here, in the Flatlands, but he knew that was an illusion.

In the first tree he had seen for miles, a crow cawed suddenly and startled him. In reflex, his hand went to his backpack, pulled out the polished, peculiarly bent piece of wood and threw it. It found its target and was back in his outstretched hand before the crow had hit the ground. Still staring at the mountains, the boy knew what he had been sent to do.

Almost There

Darren Wheatley

Out of the plane of the ecliptic, the sensors can't really convey the absolute majesty of it all. It's been so long; we've come so far. I imagine a tear, a tiny jewel of happiness swirling with regret, and though I'm consumed with the sheer weight of our achievement, I mourn once again the inevitable loss of my humanity. Of course, it will be different for the others. Deep within my hold, they sleep. I have harboured them, fed them, kept them safe and now, finally, I am to deliver them to their new Eden. And then I shall end.

Almost There   *Jenni Doherty*

A cluster of girls gathered on the dance floor in front of him. Tall, fat, short, thin shapes; dancing, butts out, moving in circular motion, galvanic orange-tinged limbs swaying without inhibition, unchained and free as they never would be in daylight. The fierceness of their glares matched by that of their joy; yellow-to-white teeth bared. Flashing laser lights picking up the dust and curdling smoke, reflecting rings in ears, noses and lips. All James could do was stare in amazement.

Outnumbered, he made his way to the bar and ordered a double. *Being single wasn't easy,* he thought.

Amazing Grace   *Steven Schusman*

He was worldly but didn't play on it. His looks were adequate but his seduction technique massaged the mind. To win at his game, and he almost always did, he had to secure the look that said "let's do it", or the equivalent fleeting touch, and that was his victory. Clothes stayed on; he was an honourable married man.

Tonight, his target was Grace, who played a similar game. She was amazing at it. In her version, the quarry was the man who thought he could resist. To win, she had to prove him wrong; and she always did.

Amazing Grace   *Neil Outram*

'How long do I have?'
   'Difficult to say, at this stage.'
   'Roughly, dear.'
   'Okay. Approximately a month, perhaps less. I'm sorry,

Grace,' said Dr Jones, lowering his head.

'That's all right, dear,' she said with a smile. 'Chin up.'

* * * *

'Everything all right?' asked Frank, struggling to stand up from the waiting-area seat. 'They give you something for your cough?'

'Yes, my dear. Absolutely fine,' said Grace, gripping his frail arm. 'Come on, the casserole will burn. Want me to run you a bath before dinner?'

'Oh, yes, love. You're too good to me, you know that?'

'I know, dear.'

Another Dimension   *Darren Wheatley*

Like a silhouette of something half-remembered, the image strained the edge of my senses and somehow, I felt haunted, stalked by something as ethereal as an idea. It spoke in words beyond hearing, painted pictures beyond sight and strolled through vistas beyond imagination. Then it was gone, leaving a desperate sense of aching absence. I cannot live without it.

Another Dimension   *Shirley Bunyan*

You were the ecstasy. You squeezed your pleasures from my recklessness; wrung my senses dry with your desire. Sublimely, we climbed to infinite heights, soared to where stars were real and wishes whispered truth. It was a world that captured and obsessed me. Too long I lingered, bliss-blinded and consumed, until you slashed my wings and I tumbled into agony.

Another Dimension   *Stephen Reilly*

'Are the antidepressants helping?'

'Hard to say. It hasn't been easy since my wife died, Doctor.'

'How are you coping?'

'I read to escape to another world. Television is too real. Sci-fi books like Ray Bradbury's *Fahrenheit Four Five One* help me stop thinking.'

'What's it about?'

'A time when everyone watches television. Reading is banned.'

'Why?'

'Because books make people think.'

Away Too Long   *Eileen Burzynska*

Faces diminished by sadness and fatigue turn towards her as she takes her place in the family pew. But the face she longs to see is lifeless beneath the lilies. God, how old they all look in their powdered wrinkles, peering at her through pale, moist eyes that accuse, 'She missed you. You missed her. You stayed away too long.'

Away Too Long   *Amanda Mair*

Morning dawned. Sunni clambered out of bed. Silently watching TV, show after show. Long after sun-up, she made cereal, sloshing milk and sugar everywhere. Lunch – cereal and biscuits. Mummy should be up. Dinner – cereal, biscuits. Best wake Mummy, there's a knock at the door.

Outside, a policeman and Granny crying. In an alleyway, Mummy lay sprawled awkwardly. Raped. Strangled. Dumped.

Back of Beyond   *Gary McMahon*

'Good grief, what happened? *Help me get him up* – did you *get* it?'

They got me up. 'Did – did *you?*'

'*You* were on ghost-watch!'

27

'I panicked! The mirror!'

'What *was* it?'

'Me!'

'That's it? That's all you got with £50,000 of electronics? Yourself in the mirror?'

'Don't you see? Play it back!'

qwertyuiop: CRASH

'Good grief!'

'It's *all* of *us!* They're . . . *trying to communicate!*'

'Can you read it?'

'Can you read it?'

'. . . DON'T . . . SMASH . . . THE MIRROR . . . OR YOU'LL . . . NEVER GET OUT!'

'Don't you see?'

'Hey, I can't get out!'

'YOU . . . ARE . . . THE PARANORMAL!'

'You great puddin', !'

'I panicked!'

qwertyuiop: CRASH

Back to School
Neil Outram

Staring into the bathroom mirror, William stroked the lengthy scar on his scalp with a quaking finger and drew in deep breaths.

Joan, his mother, watched from the doorway, distracted by memories flooding her consciousness: the racist knife attack, hospital beds, pessimistic conversations with doctors and months of rehabilitation. Finally, her brave boy was ready to resume living.

'Are you ready?' she asked.

William gripped his walking stick and turned to her. 'I d-d-don't want to g-go.'

'I know,' she replied with a forced smile.

'I hate m-m-maths.'

Joan laughed and then helped him downstairs, quietly crying tears of joy.

Black Magic   *Karen Jones*

He pressed the pin into his doll's heart, twisted an arm, stamped on a leg. His grin revealed yellow teeth, gold fillings and a blackened soul. She winced at the pains he had sent, cursed his name, then threw her doll on the fire.

'Witch!' he screamed as the flames fed on his flesh.

Her whisper kissed his ear: 'Amateur.'

Black Magic   *Jenni Doherty*

Now naked from her golden gown, would she be that chosen one to melt delicious on his tongue?

She lay there waiting, smooth and silky with curves of glossy dark. So subtly perfumed; such elegant decadence and desired by all.

It only took a moment for him to devour her completely, her dusky tempting truffles irresistible.

'Fancy another?' the confectioner teased.

Blue   *Roy Everitt*

She always wore denim when she passed his window. He looked forward to seeing her, and when she glanced in, her eyes were denim, too, or sky. Now she placed her bag on the counter:

'Somewhere warm. Where the sun shines, and the sea is . . .'

He smiled. In the bag, next to their passports, he saw a new swimsuit. Blue.

Blue *Mark Buchanan*

'Every night it's the same: a nightmare to start, but the end is beautiful. A tiger comes over the wall, staring and walking towards me. Not scared, I embrace it and everything goes blue. Then I wake.'

'Would you look at these cards and tell me what you see?'

'Just nondescript splurges.'

'You appear to have red/blue colour-perception difficulties.'

Blue *Ali Froud*

Annie's heart thumped as she hurried along the platform. She wanted to get there first. They had agreed 1.30pm, Victoria Station. He would wear blue. Oh, he was there already. Sky-blue anorak, tracksuit bottoms and trainers, and on his balding head, a blue baseball cap. Annie strolled nonchalantly past, vowing never to go on another blind date.

Blue *Jenni Doherty*

Tiny mountains of silver dust scatter around me. Green, by a swirl, ruffles trees and grass. Yellow for sunlight and Mummy's hair. Dull brown for boots and puppies' tails, black for cats and scary nights, red for smiles and apples bright. But my favourite, little stubby blue, is for water and sky and the colour that was my daddy's eyes.

Blue Moon *Mark Buchanan*

Brilliant pools of laser light burst the darkness of the hidden new moon. Sweeping the vast curved surface, they scatter the shadows and paint a flickering dance across the craters and bleached plains.

I did promise her the moon; but with one cold look, she

frosted my heart to a comet's core. Turning, sucking air through her teeth, she walked away.

'But the moon?' I called after her. She never looked back.

I see her now, far above the world; a picture I used to keep in my wallet. I can even read my name up there, on her tattoo.

Body Language *Darren Wheatley*

In the close afternoon heat, her scent hung heavy in the moist air. Unbidden, images flowed through my mind as I read the signals. An ancient script, as old as humanity itself, revealed itself to me in its full, natural splendour.

'Time of death, approximately seven-fifteen,' I announced to my assistant. 'Blood work and prints by close of play, please.'

Body Language *Karen Jones*

He kissed the tiny hollow at her throat, then slid his tongue down to the valley between her breasts. With each kiss, each stroke, he heard her breathing falter, felt her body shiver with anticipation and desire.

She shivered at his repulsive touch, held her breath to stem the nausea, closed her eyes and prayed it would soon be over.

Body Language *Stephen Reilly*

Her body is so beautiful to him, redolent of art, music and musk. She has assumed angelic form, spread in repose. She is still, ecstasy spent, her skin glistening. He carries her gently to the room, unlocks the door and lays her down. He arranges her limbs just as he had done with the others he had sacrificed to the voices.

Body Language *Rachiel Key*

Never in my wildest dreams did I think this would happen. Both hands have found their way to each other's back. Our faces, about an inch apart . . . I could feel him breathing heavily at my cheek; I wonder what his next move will be. Frank nervously parted his lips, inching closer to me. I closed my eyes and suddenly, 'Aaachooo!'

Body Language *Robert Capps*

Hands often feel awkward when we first meet a stranger. Will they notice mine? Do I grasp the hand and vigorously pump up and down? Or clasp arms around them, kissing both cheeks, like a close family member?

It is then that I feel the long thin cane. Seems both of us are blind. Wonder if he knows I am . . .

Broken *Lynda Kenny*

The necklace had been a present from her grandmother on her wedding day, a single strand of perfect pearls. She had worn them to the most important occasions of her life – the christenings, the weddings, and her grandmother's funeral.

But not today. As she signed this piece of paper, the pearls that she had loved – like her marriage – lay broken.

Broken *Amanda Mair*

Sue was a radiant bride. She fluttered around her guests, gushing from the compliments. Alone now with her husband, she caressed his head between her breasts. He shoved angrily. Flirting? No, she hadn't been flirting. The pain shocked, the blood frightened and choked.

'I'm sorry. Don't tell. It'll never happen again,' he whispered as she was carried to the ambulance.

Broken *Perry Gretton*

She'd bought him the train set for Christmas. It was his favourite toy. Becoming so engrossed in it, he lost track of time. Now it lay strewn around the room. Her heart thumped as she recovered the pieces.

'Come on out,' she said. 'I won't get angry again.'

He cowered under the table.

'You've broken it!' he began to sob.

Broken *Darren Wheatley*

And then it came to me; lightning jolt ratcheting across my creased, careening brain. Deep, rolling thunder followed as the heavy downpour dashed itself across rattling window-panes. Deep, soul-sucking breaths; sharp, earthy tang of fresh-squeezed rain cleansed the cramped confines of my singing, stinging mind. I saw the truth at last. It was too late. You were broken.

Broken *Miriam Heinbuch*

Silence. Noise. All at once, in my head. The noise comes from a lullaby of distant screams. My screams. Walls, closing in. Reducing me to a single spot in my brain, screaming, 'Stop it! Please, somebody stop it! There he is. Hold me! Save me . . .'

'What's up, love? Did you forget to take your meds again?'

I keep falling . . .

Broken *Lee Henderson*

'I'll not be bothering you again, lad,' he rasped, sidling out the room's one door. Glancing back, wisps of smoke curling into the chill night, Dane Fredricks wiped the tears that came unbidden as he viewed the picture of a son born years back amongst love, captured now in a future embrace. Needles, silver foil, rictus grin, ambulance light.

By Myself   *Eileen Burzynska*

To look backwards with no reminders and forwards with no encouragement; no-one to walk next to, no-one to laugh with, no-one to say, 'Do you remember? Look at that! What shall we do tomorrow?' No-one to share a mango, bring a drink, enjoy a meal with. I lie in my empty double bed and I do not make any plans.

By Myself   *Stephen Reilly*

Within, I perceive my body, the world and you. You prove that I am. Beauty resides in uniqueness, in you and me. We have never been before and will never be again. Freedom is our birthright and its misuse our damnation. But together, in all that we may be, the flame of hope for our salvation burns more brightly still.

By Myself   *Christopher Spalding*

'Have you seen my new shirt?'
    'Hanging up.'
    'Cufflinks?'
    'Top drawer.'
    'Is the iron on? I need to press my trousers.'
    'I did that while you were in the shower.'
    'Okay, okay. Where's my jacket?'
    'Will you *please* hurry up!'
    'What for?'
    'You've always been late for everything! I'm not waiting any longer.'
    Then she left me: I hadn't changed.

Cards

Darren Wheatley

Haggard and unshaven, Jeremy stumbled in late. All-night poker had taken its toll once more. Far from that early success, he was now over three grand down. Logging on, his inbox held an invitation from Mr Grey to visit his office.

'Jenkins, this behaviour cannot continue,' intoned the dour Grey. 'I'm afraid I'll have to hand you your cards.'

Cards

Arthur Chappell

I'm strapped to a firework, wearing a cap-a-bells with a bladder on a stick in my tied hands. The fuse paper burns. The Tarot Cards had come up *Fool, Moon* and *Death*.

Rather literal, I thought, until I saw the *Hanged Man* in the fortune-teller's garden and realised he was a serial killer, just as he knocked me out.

Cards

Karen Jones

'What do you see?' they implore. Pleading eyes, excited squeals. 'Health, wealth, happiness?'

Frightened frowns, whispered voices.

'Death, penury, misery?'

This is what I see: a pack of cards I won at the fair; a line of gullible fools, too lazy to deal their own destinies; my own smiling face reflected back in a box full of silver bribes.

Carrier Bags

Arthur Chappell

My bag split open in front of Mrs Gregson, yards from my house. My church-going neighbour helped me to pick up my sex toys. I dreaded her denouncing me throughout the community. The vibrator still had a price tag on it.

Mrs Gregson whispered to me, 'They're ten per cent cheaper at Maximus.'

I decided to invite her to the party that Saturday.

Carrier Bags
Carolyn Roberts

Every September, Professor Beatson took his yellowing notes from a cupboard and carried them to class in a dusty carrier bag. Each year, he noted the incredulous expressions on the students' faces as he entered, a shabby, sorrowful old man. And as he faced his ambitious audience and began the familiar lecture, he remembered that he, too, once had dreams.

Carrier Bags
Nicky Philips

Clearing out drawers, Sadie glimpsed episodes from her life.

The psychedelic 1969 carrier spoke of carefree, fun-filled days. Bermudas and Ryes evoked memories of idyllic holidays. Then Henley, her honeymoon. Was that rustling the patter of tiny feet in the shoe-shop carriers? Cheap supermarket bags stood for humdrum times. Finally, discovering the green/gold Knightsbridge ones, Sadie began to blush.

Carrier Bags
Karen Jones

He sealed the powder in plastic bags and slipped them into packages destined for government offices, hospitals, schools – because children in pain would wound more consciences – and a few individual addresses: personal vengeance for past wrongs.

The ensuing epidemic would be some small compensation for the tainted blood he had received. "First do no harm" was no longer his credo.

Carrier Bags   *Eileen Burzynska*

'Very sorry, no alcohol on sale in Warsaw today.'

'?'

'Pope's visit.'

'Yes, I know. I have a house full of thirsty journalists!'

'No soft drinks, either. Nothing in a glass bottle.'

'?'

'Molotov cocktails.'

'!'

'Yes, we agree. It's ridiculous. Go on, then. Just don't get caught.'

I clank furtively down the road with my carrier bags of Coke.

Casting Doubt   *Mark Buchanan*

The mountains roar their reply to Hypotenuse's hammer blows as he fixes the last copper rivet in time to the incantations of the priestesses. Giant bronze breasts gleam dully in the glow of the sinking sun; they reflect the last golden rays around him as he gives a final polish.

Titan limbs groaning, the bronze goddess stirs. She opens her eyes, gazes at him and softly whispers, 'My love.' Then screams: 'You bitches!'

Her lips curve like scimitars as she sees those who ordered the sacrificial leap of Hypotenuse's betrothed – into the white-hot crucible to flux the sacred metal.

Casting Doubt   *Julieann Campbell*

Once, I imagined I caught his scent as she tossed back her raven black hair and cursed my wretched, sinister mind. They'd never do that to me. I would have noticed the signs . . .

'I'll collect you from work, drive you for groceries. Oh, and I've brought you that silky second-hand dress you've always wanted . . .'

All the signs were there, but I chose to ignore them, revel in her infrequent company instead.

As best friends, we cruised home, music blaring, laughing and gossiping like teenagers until all at once, mid-conversation, she accidentally called me by his name. That rare, all-encompassing name.

Casting Doubt   *Andrew Clark*

Alexei discovered it while cleaning the bathroom. In the plughole, amongst the matted hairs: *dark matter.*

Feverishly, he searched. It was everywhere: in the broom cupboard, behind the sofa. In the wardrobe, amongst Maria's panties.

His superiors were sceptical; his wife more so. But Alexei rejoiced. Late at night in the physics department, he teased out the clandestine equations, shaped them into a theory to change everything. He published. The doubters closed their ears, derided him, thrust him from their circle.

Maria despaired, but Alexei's bliss was unbroken: when he showed them the plughole, his triumph would be sweeter still.

Casting Doubt   *Liz Gallagher*

It is 8.00am. She wants a boiled egg. The sand in the timer is green. She lifts the egg timer and declares it not to be moving. He lifts it and says it is moving. He says that she is too impatient, even with an egg timer. They both watch the grains of sand. Seconds later, there is no movement. He says it is airtight and should not happen. He shakes the egg timer – sideways, downwards, upwards – the grains begin to move. She gives the two fingers to the egg timer, gets her coat and buys a croissant en route.

Changeling   *Arthur Chappell*

'When did you realise you were adopted?'

'It was obvious. My parents were really tall and flightless. I never could bury my head in the sand, either.'

'Oh, well, never mind, son. Welcome home. Your brother's coming, too.'

'I have a brother?'

'Yes. He found life as an emperor penguin a bit too cold. He flies in tomorrow. Cuckoo! Cuckoo!'

Changeling   *Eileen Burzynska*

The fairy arrived with an ill-favoured child, struggling and grimacing in a cage. I flung protective arms round my own docile and angelic toddler asleep in his crib.

'You shall not take my child!' I screamed.

'Your child?' sneered the fairy. 'You never noticed the switch at his birth. But don't you worry. You can have him back and welcome!'

Christmas Stocking   *Mark Buchanan*

Having overindulged on port and blue cheese that Christmas Eve, I settled with a wish into a star-filled night of steamy dreams.

The beautiful green Medusa girl's prehensile dreadlocks tugged and tickled while she quietly hissed her soft sibilance. I woke but was delighted to find her stockinged legs lying across my chest. Still in the throes of dreamy passion, I grasped and kissed the legs and was rewarded by an answering, tightly entwining embrace.

As my ribs began to crack, I discerned there was no body attached to the leg that had somehow coiled itself around, enveloping me.

Christmas Stocking   *Ali Froud*

The fire lit the room with a warm glow. The decorations sparkled and Molly surveyed the room with satisfaction. She picked up two large socks and set about filling them. Sugar mice and chocolate money, a doll for Mary and a car for Tom, painting books, a pair of socks each and oranges. The door opened and Bert peered in.

'What are you doing, love?'

'Filling the stockings. The twins will be so excited in the morning.'

'Molly, the twins are all grown-up now, remember? We're going to Tom's for dinner tomorrow. Come on, let's get you to bed.'

Christmas Stocking   *Darren Wheatley*

'Bright red fishnets? Bright fuckin' red fishnets! I must've been a right git in a previous life or summink to 'ave got lumbered with a prat like you as an oppo!'

'But what was I s'posed to do? The wife wears tights most of the year round, an' these were only lyin' about from her works-do the uvver night.'

'That's just fuckin' great! Well, I s'pose they'll just 'ave to do. 'Ere, stick this on.'

'Okay, this is a robbery! 'Ands where I can see 'em and no funny business, if you know what's good for your 'elf.'

Christmas Stocking   *Lynda Kenny*

He crept down the stairs and into the room. Firelight guided him, and there, among the folded things, was a stocking that said "Mum".

He was six when his father died. Shushed feelings; they said he was too young. But he remembered.

But six years had passed and now his mother had another man. A man that made her happy. But he had heard the arguments, late into the night. About him. A problem child. So he put his little gift into the sack. A garish red lipstick he thought she might like, and maybe then, she would keep him. He hoped!

Climbing
Darren Wheatley

I called and told my boss I was taking the rest of the week off. He didn't argue. Natalie was coming round to pick up the rest of her things tonight and I needed to be very drunk. I didn't have to tell him that, though; he'd probably drive her round himself.

Maybe I should look for a new job.

Climbing
Gavin Damerell

Releasing his grip of the bars, Ben sank to the floor. It was no use; he was trapped. But though he knew there was no chance of escape now, he giggled to himself. For he knew it was only a matter of time before he was big enough to climb over the bars and out of his cot to freedom.

Clipped Wings
Estelle Kirk

Dawn rose, pearl-white and cold, as angels circled Saint Peter's. Pope Borgia cursed and sent forth his cringing gargoyles. They seized Angelus and clipped his wings, then held up their bloodied shears in triumph. While feathers fell as soft as thoughts, Angelus plummeted through earth and stone, towards earth's fire. "Devillius", they called him, so we wouldn't heed his screams.

Clipped Wings   *Mark Burns*

The heavyweight decider erupted midway through the third round. Sam and Joe, seated side by side, crouched forward, glued to the action unfolding before them. Joe roared and Sam groaned as Bonecrusher Bates pummelled his opponent onto the ropes.

Just then, Sam's mother appeared at the doorway.

'Enough!' she snapped. 'I told you already: homework first, play computer games later.'

Clipped Wings   *Dan Purdue*

Alistair clipped his hens' wings, tired of returning escapees to their enclosure.

The next morning, blinking away tears, he piled their corpses into his father's wheelbarrow. He saw their gaping throats and staring, sightless eyes. He saw where the mink had bent the wire mesh. He saw the earth, ravaged by the hens' frenzied, futile attempts to outrun their killer.

Closing Time   *Eileen Burzynska*

There's always an old boy sitting at a corner table, trying to look as though he belongs to the adjacent group, gesturing happily to imaginary acquaintances, making his pint last as long as possible.

At the end of the evening, though, when everyone is moving on and staggering out, he stays there until he is cleared out with the ashtrays.

Closing Time   *Anne Rainbow*

Beside Laura's bed, next to the alarm clock, which would wake no-one tomorrow, a neat row of bottles stood to attention, their caps upturned amid puffs of cotton wool. Laura swallowed the last capsule and drained her glass. She re-read her note and then, leaning back on her silk pillow, closed her eyes and let the darkness engulf her.

Closing Time   *Jenni Doherty*

Distance between us: twelve pound fifty, one hour and forty minutes, one taxi, a front door, a flatmate, a skin colour, an accent, musical taste, a lighter – or would you prefer a match?

Different drinks. Different faiths. Different circumstances . . . Nah, it would never work; you don't have an alarm clock (although coffee helps).

Okay, meet you outside, babe.

Colour   *Arthur Chappell*

'Gay! My God, David. Since when? And how could you pop out of the closet so casually during our Christmas dinner like that? Apologise to the Pilkingtons at once. You've got kids. You should have told Mary before the wedding.'

'Don't go homophobic on me, Dad. I said I'm going *grey*.'

'Sorry, son. My hearing aid needs fixing.'

Colour   *Nicky Philips*

It was the bane of her life. Adolescence in the seventies was hard enough without this. Why her? Friends started to drop her. Boys passed her by. Money wasn't an issue, yet this shame would cling forever. If only she could change things. But she was the only girl in town whose parents refused to get a colour TV.

Colour *Anne Rainbow*

Gert grabbed George's arm.

'Oh, look! There's Barbra Streisand. What a beautiful rich lavender colour! And Marilyn Monroe, in apricot cream-washed green.'

George, too, was impressed.

'Wow! Lynn Anderson in a cream-edged deep pink and Chris Evert in melon-orange blushing red.'

'Oh, so much choice,' said Gert.

'Your choice, love. Your bouquet,' said George, kissing her gently.

Coming Home *Nathalie Boisard-Beudin*

Coming home after his travels, he was surprised to find his parents withered and a lodger in his bedroom. His surprise was even greater when his otherwise delighted parents told him – in a rather roundabout and embarrassed way – that they had disposed of his things. How could they have?

'But, Ulysses, dearest, you were gone for twenty years . . .'

Coming Home *Eileen Burzynska*

Shuffling shoulders through hot, windy subterranean passages to squeeze between knees, stomachs and briefcases, lurching and lunging through the dark; then thrust out into the cold air to pick your way in pinching shoes through the punishing wetness of a wintry night, past leering, steamed-up windows to your empty room for one. There must be more than this.

Coming Home *Moses Abukutsa*

She packed her tears in her heart. He looked pensive, but her eyes were resolved.

44

Yesterday, he battered her at the bar before her friends. Now he was pensive, pensive because she was embracing her suitcase, her destination home. All the shame of his violence against her body would end because she was coming home. Home is home.

Coming Home   *Jenni Doherty*

I remember hideaways and doorstep gropes, giggle winks and daisy chains. Remember love and life and oh how we laughed and learned to somersault with cider draught and tongue assault. Intimacies recaptured hugging warmth. Village back-doors always open. The smell of baking bread. Moments that we all once shared then forgot. I call it back once more to return to me.

Commitment   *Amanda Mair*

Eliza stared out the window seeing not what was but what had been. She wondered why she had ever made Jeremy promise to marry her. Nowadays, it didn't matter, but they were the "old stock". They'd made a promise they couldn't break: "till death do us part". She could do nothing but hope and dream for their time to end.

Commitment   *Maureen Wilkinson*

I'd never seen my father cry and now his face dissolved like melting wax; the corners of his mouth trembled. The downward lines were channels to guide rivers of tears to his chin.

I put my cheek against his and our tears mingled. 'You've got to carry on without her.'

'Why? There's no reason – no reason.'

'There's always me, Dad.'

Commitment

Nathalie Boisard-Beudin

'I shall always love you,' he said, and in a certain sense he spoke the truth.

She let herself be swept away and their love was passionate and riotous. But short-lived.

"Forever" can prove a fleeting notion and "ever" a rather brief period. In the present case, it did not extend beyond sunset.

But what is eternity to a butterfly?

Commitment

Felicity McCall

'Remember me?'

Middle-aged anonymity masks the face thrust over the rim of the café coffee cup. The eyes are bright, imploring her to remember shared intimacy.

She smiles. Reels back years of places, spaces, searching for a clue.

'Remember me?'

She cannot kill his hope. She answers, 'Course I do!'

And never knew if she had been untrue.

Crashing In

Karen Jones

While he was at work she wandered around in his bathrobe, lay on his bed, dabbed his cologne on her slender wrists. She played at living with him. She had sneaked out one morning and had his keys copied, returning to his bedroom with fresh croissants and secret smiles. He had woken up with that hungry look in his eyes, grabbed her and made love to her again. Today she saw the note: *Love you always.* The unfamiliar writing blurred as the truth came crashing in, and her fantasy world, like her heart, was crushed to dust.

Crashing In *Darren Wheatley*

Got booted out of my digs last night. Well, the landlord was a git, knew money was tight. Maybe we could've sorted it out, like, if he hadn't hassled me while I was pissed. My advice: never bunk above a pub. Anyway, bloke down the bookies says I can borrow his old camper van. You know, one of them trendy Volkswagen things. No more drink driving – just park up outside any boozer I like. Mind you, he reckons the brakes aren't up to much and the steering's a bit dodgy. Still, like he says, it'll be all right for crashing in.

Crashing In *Liz Gallagher*

I am fifteen. A woman-in-red. Black clogs are the finishing touch. It is snowing. We walk to the Fairyland of Romance. We whip off the clogs and bang them against trees, dislodging hardening snow. Inside Fairyland, my head presses against a new-found white shirt. We slow-number. Two hearts hula-hoop. Eyelashes tickle. Feet mix. Laughter bursts. Couples bend over as Beauty, my dog, pounds his snowy-furry way towards me. Delirious paws are beating my chest. My dancing partner falls. There is a paw mark on a white shirt and a lift home in a Mini with Beauty in the front seat.

Crossing Over *Darren Wheatley*

It all happened so easily. Our eyes met, our hands touched, our souls melded. In the sleazy excitement of a cheap city hotel, we fucked all night on polyester sheets and I felt as if my heart would burst. In the morning, I awoke, curled snugly into his brawny arms. Telling the wife was not going to be so easy.

Crossing Over *Perry Gretton*

She's heading my way. Oh, shit! I'll have to cross the road and pretend I didn't see her. I really can't take any more of her garrulous accounts of her family's tiresome problems. Who the hell's interested, anyway? Believe me, I'm not. Uh-oh, she's seen me. Too late, I'll have to speak to her.

'Mum, it's me. Don't cross over.'

Cryogenic Crisis *Sarah Star*

Deep in the dark caves of immortality, I lay sleeping the sleep of the damned. Safe within my tomb, awaiting my time. Within the crevasses of my mind, something stirred, like a worm in the crack of the ice, in the blink of an eye. 'Twas the noise of distant thunder that broke in on my tranquillity and the pain of blood coursing through my veins once more. Could they not leave me in peace?

My cold hand reached for my sword as I heard the call.

'Awake, once and future king! England needs you!'

Cryogenic Crisis *Lynda Kenny*

The procedure had gone exactly to plan. The Medibots stood back as if to admire their handiwork and watched as the patient opened her eyes. This had been no ordinary operation; in fact, it was the first of its kind anywhere in the world. The Medibots had been certain of the outcome; they had come a long way with their biomech research. They had followed the patient's wishes to the letter and hoped to interact with her when the meds had worn off. The Medibots looked perplexed when the head attached to the network of wires began to scream.

Crystal Ball *Mark Buchanan*

I refract and scatter starlight, projecting faint glimmering spectrums onto dark surfaces of dead frozen worlds. I'm classified as "black dwarf", but none venture close enough to see that I'm really transparent crystalline carbon. The flickering rainbows escaping my powerful gravitational pull sing my forgotten history. White dwarf, planetary nebula, red giant, yellow dwarf; I was once called Sol.

Crystal Ball *Roy Everitt*

'We don't have a crystal ball,' said the weatherman, 'but I do know yesterday was sunny.'

'How?' said the small child.

'We measure it.'

'How?'

'We have a sunshine recorder – a glass sphere that focuses the sunlight onto a card and burns a trace.'

'What's a safeer?'

'A sphere. Like a glass ball.'

'Like a . . . crystal ball?'

'Okay, who's next?'

Cult *Arthur Chappell*

'Nudity is forbidden in the Ashram, Sanyassin.'

'What about the orgy?'

'Fornication is forbidden. The Master has heard of AIDS. He declared us celibate at midnight last night.'

'But I left a chastity-practising monastic order after forty years when I learned that you practised group sex.'

'You arrived too late, friend. Sorry.'

'Bollo—'

'No swearing in the Ashram, Sanyassin.'

Cult   *Teresa Stenson*

'Let's start our own cult.'

Her eyes are fast, crazy. I am filled with excitement: anything for her.

'Yes. What kind?'

She sighs backwards, arms lolling behind her on hot grass.

'What? Oh, I don't know. You're so practical, Jane.'

The urgency is lost. I watch her face, closed eyes untroubled by the sun, and move into the shade.

Cult   *Darren Wheatley*

The light in her eyes took on a deep orange hue as it reflected the glowing hot coals languidly burning before her unwavering features. The moment she had waited so longingly for, the very purpose she had been put on this earth for, had finally arrived. Only the chosen few could ever know ecstasy such as this.

'Chilli sauce with that?'

Cult   *Lynda Kenny*

He watched as they looked for clues in churches, mote stilled in sunlit air. He watched as they looked for clues in galleries, air-brushed, canvas bare. He watched as they looked for clues in libraries, huge tomes, nothing much to share.

He laughed as they tried to understand the bible, and knew his fallen words would catch them there.

Damage   *Eileen Burzynska*

She thought it logical to have her husband's car scrapped when he died, rather like throwing it on the burial pyre. But as she watched it being hoisted onto the truck and secured with a spike driven through the roof, another crack in her heart gaped, and she wanted to jump up and go with the car to be crushed.

Damage
Lee Henderson

'Hmmm, collateral damage. Did it suffer?' he asked, peering at the toddler.

I'd spent precious minutes assuring this young mother her child would be fine. Now both lay dead from shrapnel wounds. Bombs are indiscriminate.

'It's a little boy. He and his mother are dead,' I hissed.

'Damage, Captain? You're the one suffering damage, not them. They're just dead.'

Darkness and Light
Karen Jones

In darkness, he covers me with kisses, wraps himself around me, makes me tremble. In darkness, he shares his secrets, his ambitions, his desires. He's mine to love, mine to touch, mine to own.

In light, we're distant, reserved, professional. In light, she clutches his arm in the picture on his desk. He holds her close, protects his family, hides his lies.

Each time I wake beside the impression he has left on my mattress, the scent he has transferred to my pillow, the words he has etched upon my mind:

'Love you.'

In the daylight, I long for darkness.

Darkness and Light
Jenni Doherty

The strange man and his black dog were just a few yards behind me. My hands were shaking. Anxiety stormed through my shivering bones. I cowered while the rain slapped my scalp and whipped my face as if angry. Dark clouds hung viciously above trees like ogres with arms outstretched. I rattled raw beneath their scary skeleton-like fingers and began to panic. It was killing me. I could smell it. Taste it. I couldn't prolong it any more. This was the only chance I had left . . . I had to face him.

'Excuse me, mister. Have ye gotta light?' I wheezed.

Darkness and Light   *Neil Outram*

Even after eighteen months, I still notice how we attract looks. Some lecherous, some intrigued, some indignant – all directed at her, and then maybe me as an after-thought because I complete the perceived bizarre spectacle.

'Where's she from?' some ask.

'England,' I reply.

'What's it like?' the same people inquire.

'Chocolate so supple yet it doesn't melt to the touch.'

They rarely notice the sarcasm.

She is neither a delicacy nor a fetish. We are different in superficial ways, but together we are whole: she is the yin, I am the yang; she is the darkness, I am the light.

Darkness and Light   *Kitty Redding*

I slide my finger along the seal to open the lid; it pops up, revealing neat rows of perfectly crafted chocolates. My favourites. I tear myself away from the enticing feast and look at the note.

'For you. Guess who?'

A mystery admirer who knows me well. I ponder a moment. I think I know. The white-chocolate strawberry-cream tempts me. Then I spy a dark fudge. My hand hovers. Wait, a milk-chocolate mound filled with caramel. Perfect! It melts on my tongue then slides down my throat. A box of love, darkness and light, bursting with potential.

Dawn

Karen Jones

He hid in the shadows the trees threw over the path. Concealed by their sombre embrace, he waited for darkness to shroud him, screen him from their search. He breathed deep and even: silent, as he had practised.

As the moon blued the clouds, he relaxed, allowed his presence to merge with the forest, to slumber in its arms. Too deep. Too soft. Far too careless.

Dawn brought the howls of dogs, alerted by his ripe, unwashed scent. Sleep caught his limbs, made them heavy. Escape would be difficult, progress slowed by drugged torpor.

And yet he knew this was his one chance. If he were returned, it would be to solitary confinement and lost hope.

He dragged his twisted mind and body along the path, cursing the night, berating the morning, pleading with the god he had forgotten. But there is no reprieve or compassion for insanity.

Dawn

Nathalie Boisard-Beudin

You have to be careful when giving names. Children do have a natural tendency to spite their parents and act contrary to their wishes. Take Dawn, for instance. By rights, she should have been a bright and early creature, rosy cheeked and full of promise. But she grew up to be something else altogether.

A pale and introverted weedy child at first; growing up, she somehow failed to blossom. She turned to a gothic-night lifestyle, shunning sunlight or anything even remotely coloured. Sleeping all day and partying all night in dark caves while her parents were at their wits' end and despairing of her future. Hope had been her middle name (after her maternal grandmother) and she wasn't promising any.

Her mother often sighed that it was lucky they hadn't named her after her husband's grandmother. After all, "Chastity" would have been unbearable . . .

Dawn
Jenni Doherty

It was good driving across the border to Donegal. Good to taste sound beer and sharp wit. It was good the way we got lost and laughed at strangers in an empty bar – deep voices, short skirts, nice toilets. An hour, a few hours, taking off as soon as we walked in. It was good that we left and landed in another place, where everyone else lived where we stood. Lucky that out of three ladies, only one of us got a ladder in our tights. Cool that we looked cool, felt great, but weren't particularly good.

But it was wonderful to see you again.

I didn't expect you to talk when you didn't speak. You kissed me, knowing what I always knew. Wonderful to meet you again, and yes, it was sad the way the weather changed, the way night and day traded off and I went home.

Desperation
Elizabeth Madden

Marie was a happy child. Size fourteen at fifteen: her peers mocked her excessive size, so she made it her business to conform; she wanted to please. By the time she was seventeen, she was size six and skeletal, but still imperfect. She's still with us, in an urn on the mantelpiece. Just a few ounces of her now.

Diplomacy
Sam Robinson

'How can we respond seriously when we've had three consecutive false alarms?' the mission chief complained to a young diplomat on the anti-terrorism desk.

Fearing a further reprimand, the diplomat decided to phrase his future intelligence so he could take credit if the information proved accurate but deny everything if it were wrong. His next tip-off came from a most reliable source and was specific as to date. He constructed his Delphic memorandum.

On the threatened morning, he stood akimbo at his office

window, gazing down the sharply sloping street towards the sparkling harbour at its foot. To his horror, he noticed a heavily bearded man park a van outside the embassy, slink from it, and ride off on a motorcycle.

The diplomat sprinted out and let the handbrake off the unlocked van. It lurched down the street, scraped a bus as it crossed the Harbour Road and exploded as it burst through the railings beyond.

He stood, breathless; convinced he'd be praised from on high for the warning he'd passed on so clearly.

Diplomacy   *Amy Rafferty*

'Say that again?' says Marie.

'Ah'm jist saying, that when you stand under that light, yer 'tache glows.'

Wullie takes a sip of his pint. Marie flinches as she waits to hear what he's going to come up with next.

'There's no missing it, Hen.'

There's a low chuckle from the men at the bar as they pick up their pints, trying to hide their smirks.

Marie tries to smile. 'I get away with it, it's blonde.'

He snorts. 'Blonde? It's a fucking 'tache. Yer needing some Immac.'

And that's it, game over. Wullie's beaming, knowing the trembling lip will start and then the tears. He's a sick wee bastard.

Tonight, he's been on his whiskey and it makes him as sour as his breath. One of the barmaids comes over, puts her arm around Marie and leads her, greetin', through to the back. The pub is silent except for the wailing coming from the staff room.

'Ach, dry yer eyes, you,' says Wullie. 'It's just a bit of friendly advice.'

Diplomacy *Teri Davis-Rouvelas*

The marketplace was packed. Kalilah stared at the throngs of people – most wearing yarmulkes – from her window. She thought of Iman and his touches. The very thing she missed most – his gentleness with her – had led to what grew now in her belly.

He'd promised to leave his wife. Kalilah listened carefully to his vows to love her and their baby forever, to move all of them some place safe. If her family ever found out . . . but they didn't talk about that.

Until they were told others knew: her father, brothers and uncles.

Adultery. Stoning. Honour killings. Words Kalilah heard her entire life, and she wondered what her father's decision would be. What would he determine to be the way to restore respectability to her family?

She heard her door open and turned to face Iman's soft, brown eyes. They moved down towards her stomach before staring past her and out at the crowded shops.

Iman tightened the explosive vest around her waist before he adjusted the heavy belt around his own. They almost matched.

Disclosure *Anne Rainbow*

Kay let the hot water run down her body, removing all traces of Vince's bodily scent. If Victor noticed her smiling, he'd take full credit; and Vince thought he was the only man in her life, too.

She turned off the tap and, reaching for a towel, saw a fingered message revealed on the steamed mirror:

Love you!
V
xxx

Distant Memories

Stephen Reilly

We stand together in crowds on Putney Bridge. The boats surge at the starter's gun, draw together and pull apart. I'd been unfaithful, my "mistress" work in far-off places. She'd "kissed" a man from Harrods; I never knew. Oars clashed. No-one sank. We haven't talked in ten years now – as long as we'd been married then – not even to say goodbye.

Distant Memories

Amanda Mair

Turning off the alarm, Jeremy drifted asleep. Eliza curled gracefully, naked against him. Her heady aroma, soft sensual lips, such bliss! Everyone had been so jealous of him.

'Just because you've retired doesn't mean lying in bed all day. There's things need doing, starting with breakfast.'

Eliza's cold shrillness pierced the depths of his reverie. Where did the beauty go?

Distant Memories

Azfarul Islam

'I miss my only daughter so much,' crooned the war veteran, brushing the picture lightly with quivering fingers. 'She was so . . . sweet.' Tears travelled down the ridges of his wrinkled face as the others watched, sharing in his loss.

A prim, professional lady staccatoed into the room and curtly called out to the man, 'It's time to go home, Father.'

Doorbell

Arthur Chappell

'Dawkins, a word please. The theme from *The Addams Family* television series is not an appropriate doorbell chime for our funeral parlour. It's rather distasteful. Business is dying. People are taking their loved ones elsewhere. Are you deliberately trying to ruin us? Let me pick the replacement chime, please.'

Happy Days Are Here Again.
'There, isn't that better?'

Doorbell   *Shonali Bhattacharya*

Forty walls as company, forty winks in store, forty thoughts before hitting the sack, eight hundred friends worldwide, accolades and trophies of achievement, a loving photograph of children, man and wife beside wife's ashes in the urn, dinner cold on plate, the clock strikes midnight when he walks outside the door and rings the bell that sings *Happy Birthday To You.*

Drip   *Carolyn Roberts*

Swinging my handbag confidently, I marched up to the shiny smart offices where my interview would take place. I paused at the entrance to admire my reflection in the glass doors. *Sassy but professional,* I thought with satisfaction.

A bird crapped on my head. The mess slid down my suit and dripped onto the ground.

I didn't get the job.

Drip   *Eileen Burzynska*

Plip!

The rain, pouring down outside, was infiltrating the bedroom again, landing percussively in the waiting bucket.

'Why don't you get that roof fixed, Clive?' fumed Claire. 'One phone call, that's all. What is it with you? It's the same with everything: no drive, no get up and go, no anything! In fact, you're a total waste of space!'

Plip!

Drunken Rant *Karen Jones*

They sat on the bench in George Square.

'Ah love you. Naw, really – ah do. Ah really, really love you. You're ma best mate. Ah 'hink you're magic, by the way. Whit's the matter, no talkin'? Aw well, fuck you, then, ya torn-faced basturt. You lookin' at me? You fuckin' lookin' at me?'

The pigeon flew away – feelings hurt.

Drunken Rant *Eileen Burzynska*

'Shit!' Leonard falls in through the door. 'Who put that fucking hallstand there?'

'No, it fucking wasn't there when I went out!'

'There's fumbrellas and stalking wicks all over the shop.'

'I'm not talking bloody bollocks! Wash yer mouth out.'

'I'm telling you that fucking hallstand was on the other side.'

'Well, you must have moved the fucking stairs, then!'

Drunken Rant *Elizabeth Madden*

'What're you lookin' at, eh? Aye, you! Ah saw ye, don't kid oan ye wurnae lookin'. Here, ah'm talkin' tae ye! C'mon, then. See you? See me? See me 'n' you, we're gaunnae gae roond the back, jaickits aff, an' hiv a squerr go an' soart this oot, ya ugly cunt!' he shouted at the mirror.

Drunken Rant *Arthur Chappell*

'We've got a problem. The prime minister's as drunk as a skunk.'

'How can you tell?'

'His policies are making sense. He actually wants to help the health service, improve education, end war and redistribute wealth, rather than just promising to do it.'

'Get him to Downing Street, discreetly. We'll send his double out to do the broadcast.'

Echoes   *Lynda Kenny*

He had been listening to the echoes of the universe expanding for years. He always found the sibilant sound strangely soothing. He imagined the vast quantities of matter moving ever outwards, creating space and time in their path. He knew the process was slowing down and he was listening to the last vestiges of creation as the momentum, created with the big bang, was lost. For three days, the instruments had been silent. Then they began again. He was the first to hear it, vaguely reminding him of someone slurping through a straw. He knew immediately what it meant.

Echoes   *Petya Mihaylova Stefanova-Gieridis*

A man hunts and fights. A woman gossips and dreams.

'I won't go out of the water, Mummy! I'll live in it; I'll turn into a mermaid and become a mother. Of the Little Mermaid. She is a mother of twaddle. Of gods. She flies off on the wings of imagination beyond any knowledge . . . If I'm tired of the fish tail, I'll go to the sea witch. And I'll turn into a wave at the end! The prince will turn into foam. The soap one. Men are like gods – they are born and die on the breasts of a woman.'

Echoes   *Andrew Clark*

Janie had asked Jack to the gallery.

'Echoes of childhood,' she said, admiring the picture as he admired her shapely behind.

She looked at him. He blushed: was it a question?

'But something . . .'

'Knowing?'

'Mmm.' There certainly was something knowing about her expression, those owlish glasses and prominent eyebrows . . .

She turned back to the picture: just a splurge of red and white paint.

'You know, I'd never have brought Graeme here. But we *understand* each other, right?' Jack wasn't sure he understood anything. He was eighteen, inexperienced, out of his depth.

'Sure.' Nervously, he took her hand in his.

Echoes   *Amy Rafferty*

I ask her if she wants me to change the channel on the TV. She gulps hard and says, 'Gaaah.'

I turn the channel.

She has trouble swallowing by herself. We make her drink from a baby's beaker, to help her regain control of the muscles in her mouth and throat. The nurse recommended it on the third day. She's been here six weeks now.

'Mum, I've got to go now.'

I give her a kiss and she wrinkles her face at me. Her good hand pats mine.

'Gahhhh,' she says

'Gahhh, Mum,' I say and kiss her again.

Effigy   *Eileen Burzynska*

He lies there, the Fifth Earl of Forth, pointy feet resting on a small dog of indeterminate breed, arms folded on his chest. Along the base are his fifteen children carved in relief, all kneeling with clasped hands. Only five survived him. His two wives, originally at his side, broke off some time in the seventeenth century. They'd had enough.

Effigy   *Arthur Chappell*

'You're nicked.'

'What for? It's a dummy of Guy Fawkes.'

'Nevertheless, you are celebrating and advocating terrorism. He tried to blow up the Houses of Parliament.'

'That was in 1605!'

'Bonfire Night celebrations are illegal now. Come quietly or you're going to Guantánamo Bay.'

'I wish he'd bloody succeeded now if this is how the law behaves today.'

'That's a confession.'

Embarrassed   *Perry Gretton*

Lately, I've taken to painting nudes. Always men. Young men. Although I pay the models well, turnover is high. I suppose it's because of the tedious nature of posing. I often wonder what their partners think afterwards, the first time they see their men get undressed in front of them, revealing my elaborate artwork. I do like to paint everything.

Embarrassed   *Maureen Wilkinson*

My new love moved rhythmically beneath me, skin like oiled silk. The musky scent of sex strong in the air as her soft moans whispered her pleasure against my ear. Blood pounded in my head and I squeezed my eyes shut. *Think of something else*, I told myself. Too late – I had lost the delicate balance between success and failure.

Embarrassed   *Maxwell Mutami*

Kudzi anxiously waited. He held his cell phone like a mirror. Monalisa rarely delayed replies. Flash! New message! Alas! Not from Monalisa, but Sheila, his wife.

'Cheat! I got you! Said you married a bee for a wife? I buzz when I talk and sting when I touch? Business trip cancelled! More buzzing and stinging tonight!'

'Gosh! Wrong recipient,' cried Kudzi.

Empty Space
Darren Wheatley

He smiled triumphantly, raised his bone-weary hands and stood basking in his own unique magnificence. Embarrassed, he knew it couldn't last. Pride was anathema to him. Occasionally, he forgot. But still, his universe was about to change in the most extraordinary way imaginable.

An instant. The first. Never again would he be able to claim to have no time.

Empty Space
Stephen Reilly

… … … … … … …
    '… … …, …?'
    '… … …, …'
… … … … … … … … … … … …, '… … … … … …?'
'…!'
'… … … …?' … …
'…!'
'…?'
'… …, … … …'
The End.

End of the Line
Darren Wheatley

A tired, stale wind stirs the dead leaves in the corner as the old man shrugs beneath yesterday's news. He remembers a time when warmth and laughter were more than just distant memories, but now each moment of indecision, each fleeting glimpse of greener pastures form nothing more than stark, painful waypoints on the route-map of ruin his life has become. A lone rat, rummaging in the corner for one last morsel, sniffs the air and is away before the rattling old loco wheezes up to the deserted platform. The fell conductor, cloaked in mist, beckons to his single passenger.

End of the Line *Jenni Doherty*

I have been traced through my gender's grace, pinned down strong in this female race. I have had that purple star stapled to my heart. I am a woman whose cradle waits for her womb to grow with sons and daughters of wind and rain. This is me. Look at me. Ready to breed. Ready to seed with another generation.

I anxiously wait for him to answer. That white coat. Grey face.

'Erm, Mrs Childers, I am so very, very sorry . . .'

I crush the little pink booties in my mind. Blood, finger, scissors. End of the line. History. Her story. Mine.

End of the Line *Ali Froud*

A hooded figure slipped over the wall and crept stealthily up the garden path. He seemed to navigate the layout of the garden as though it were familiar territory.

I watched from the bedroom window. I could make out the shapes of my washing flapping in the breeze and I could just about see what the stranger couldn't, PC McQuade hiding behind the shed. As the thief reached up to unpeg my new white silk knickers from the washing line, I heard the policeman shout:

'You're nicked, you knicker-nicker. It's the end of the line for you, sonny!'

End of the Line *Christopher Spalding*

The slide on Patrick's pistol locked back, ejecting the last shell case, which chinked across the marble floor and came to rest against a solitary, unspent 9-mm cartridge. The air was thick with tear gas and burnt cordite as, through the plastic screen of his gas mask, his eyes traced a path.

Broken glass crunched beneath his boots as he crossed the room to the window, mindfully stepping over each lifeless body he encountered. Outside the Post Office, police cars lined the street, lights flashing, shielding the huntsmen as they took aim. He bent down and picked up the final bullet.

Expectations *Eileen Burzynska*

He spent the night of their second wedding anniversary sprawled on the bathroom floor, snoring. She sighed as she scrubbed his vomit off the stair carpet, remembering the angelic, fresh-faced young man who had vowed shyly to honour her with his body. There it lay. She kicked the door shut on him and went to bed with her crossword puzzle book.

Expectations *Jill Paiton*

Lucy had dressed before the dormitory bell heralded the start of another predictable day. Her mother was getting re-married today. At last, she would be sprung from the orphanage.

Reverend Mother appeared in front of Lucy with a letter. Lucy read her mother's tearstained handwriting.

'So sorry, darling,' it read, 'Len said he is marrying me, not my kids.'

Expectations *Stephen Reilly*

'What do you see yourself doing in five years time, Mr Ponsonby-Smythe?'

'The natural step is to be chief executive of the company.'

'Why?'

'Because it's what I have been trained to be.'

'But would you *like* to be chief executive?'

'Ahm . . . well . . . I really wanted to be a bricklayer, but there just weren't the opportunities when I was growing up.'

Falling Rain *Kitty Redding*

Incessant rain soaks in deep. Sighing, John persists in his heavy task. Blistered hands slipping on the wet spade digging deeper, jabbing into sodden clay. Cold rainwater mingled with salty tears. He leans on his spade, overcome, his hulking frame hunched, heaving shoulders, outpouring grief.

Girding himself, he determines to finish – thud – scrape – pound – gritted teeth. The ground an opening cavern, black, vacuous. His mind a whirr of memories, happy days – gone. Hopes and dreams cruelly dashed.

The back door creaks open, disturbing his reverie. Ashen faced, he turns to his wife.

'Haven't you buried that bloody budgie yet?'

Falling Rain *Estelle Kirk*

The Hadza women crept forward through the parched grass and left their meagre offerings of food under the swollen-bellied Baobab tree. Cries of anguish came from within. Jackals circled somewhere close by, too fearful of the sound to come closer. With heavy hearts, the women stole away into the gloomy night. They glanced up at the swirling mass of clouds above and raised their twisted fingers in a sign to deny bad omens.

As dawn came, tired feet stepped out of the wide fissure in the tree. The woman held up her newborn child to be washed in the falling rain.

Falling Rain   *Sarah Star*

Rain fell constantly, washing the coal dust down the cobbled lanes, seeping into the stone-cold houses, leaving behind the smell of damp and the silver glint of wet against the slate.

Ma was scrubbing at the blackened step when we heard the ground rumble. Shouts of 'The school!' caused us to run out, slipping down the street. We stood, stunned, looking at it covered by the slagheap, like a burial mound.

'Those innocent children!' cried Ma, gently touching my head, because I should have been there that day and now my friends were gone. And still the rain fell.

Falling Rain   *Jenni Doherty*

Seán descended the cobblestone steps to the eerie water, now tinselled with twinkling frost. He could see waves caressing the rocks. Ecstasy in union. Rhythmical sounds. Utopia. This was power. This is power. Water was stronger than life. Water was stronger than flesh.

The plunge sent waves circulating for a few seconds, yet the next smacked the rocks as before. Towering bullies crashed against these vast victims, who stood undisturbed in silent dignity and indifference. They had stolen another innocent loner. A life. A beauty. A youth. But he was free. He was home.

It started to rain again . . .

Fire   *Perry Gretton*

The captain removed the cigarette from my mouth and I heard him stride away. I waited as sweat coursed down my body.

'Fire!'

A volley of clicks.

'What's wrong?' shouted the captain.

'No bullets, Captain,' replied a soldier.

Fools! As if I would supply both guns *and* ammunition.

'Captain,' I said, 'remember the rules. Now you must let me go.'

Fire   *Stephen Reilly*

He was nearing the front but couldn't hear what was said to the others as they moved away. He knew what would be said to him. But no word was spoken as the finger pointed. He smiled and moved behind the iridescent veil. Pushed from behind, he fell, his least troubled thought *if only* as the eternal flames engulfed him.

Fire   *Shirley Bunyan*

Miriam stared incredulously at the screen. *RIFE*. Her meticulous training was evident.

'Emergency Code A, Captain! I repeat, Code A!'

She slumped on the desk, thanking God for twenty-first-century technology allowing her to remotely lock the infected aircraft.

When they told her about the burnt bodies, she could barely comprehend it. Her dyslexia had never been a problem before.

Fish Out of Water   *Colin Biggs*

Her sisters circled the harbour gate, crying still, chanting their farewell song.

She hid the fear within her heart as, flexing her spine, she leapt from the swell onto the breakwater. Gasping, tasting air for the first time, she looked around the rubbish-strewn beach and the headland, shielding her eyes from the evening sunlight.

Instinctively, she shuddered at the drunken, leering crowd, drawn towards her by her lustrous, golden hair draped across perfect white breasts. Her lithe, shining tail shocked them to silence.

'I am Elyssene of the deep world,' she told the humans. 'You are killing our children.'

Fitness Class   *Richard Chalu*

'Leotards?' he repeated. She was gorgeous.

'Yes, please. Size ten and blue if possible. My fitness class is full of reds and blacks.'

'Reds and blacks? They're *so* last year.'

The young woman laughed. His charm never failed. In a flash, Bernard had gathered every blue leotard he stocked.

'Best thing to do is try them all to see which one's the most comfortable. The changing room's over there.'

'Thanks. I'll do that.'

Bernard slipped into the back office and clicked "Record". Multiple cameras behind the two-way mirrors watched silently. Another day's update for his website was in the bag.

Fitness Class   *Darren Wheatley*

We had fitness class today. They did a whole load of tests on us: comprehension, logic, empathy, stuff like that. Then they asked a bunch of questions about our home life – where we live, what our parents do for a living, what we eat. Then we had to wait while they looked at the results.

I didn't make it. Turns out I'm not "psychologically inclined" enough. I wasn't the only one. Kate Simmons failed as well, and her family's rich. Mum cried when I told her. I'm booked in for sterilisation next Thursday. It won't hurt. So they tell me.

Free   *Perry Gretton*

Freedom beckons. She carefully removes the rings, the wristwatch, the simple gold necklace and earrings and places them neatly behind her feet. As the 6.42 express hurtles towards the platform, she steps forward.

'No, you don't!'

She is jerked back as the blast of air from the passing train billows her skirt into her despairing face. A new nightmare begins.

Freefall   *Richard Chalu*

Darling Richard

You always said extreme sports would kill me. My parachute's failed, so you were right, son! There's two thousand feet to go and there are things I must tell you in this note before I die.

First, George; he's not your real father. Eurgh! Just fallen through cloud. I'm soaked!

Anyway, you're the secret lovechild of the late Baron Uberschlong. Many thought he died impoverished, but no. He hid his enormous wealth from the Nazis during WWII. You're his only descendant. There's gold worth millions buried in the Père Lachaise cemetery. It's all yours. It's under the grave marked . . .

Free Spirit   *Tamzin Mole*

She always began a séance with a prayer to calm her customers before turning off the lights. Smiling into the darkness, she asked, 'Come spirits . . . if you will.'

The company fell silent, their hands clasped ever more tightly on the table. The chandelier suddenly trembled as if drawn into life. Silently, the medium pulled the thread again. Her audience cried out in alarm.

'They are among us . . .'

Then she felt the thread snap. But the quaking did not cease. It rose in intensity until the ceiling plaster rained angrily upon them and the table groaned beneath them.

'Yes. We are here . . .'

Free Spirit
Jenni Doherty

We are born of lands and many hands. We are stretched and fetched through illustrious histories, loves and lore. Touched by the shorthand of our nerves, stories, imaginations – in the middle of nowhere, at the circle of everything in a spill of spirit.

I stand seduced by earthly smells, drown in its colour of truth. I want to keen and howl. I want to embrace all this and surface hot with clay. I want to bury fingernails deep to dig out taunt of ancestral call to soul burst free and I will love my unborn children more than them.

Free Spirit
Liz Gallagher

She has attempted to be artistic, knowingly and unknowingly. This time, she worked with clay to make a bust of a primitive man with high cheekbones and sunken eyes. When the art school closed, she collected him, put him in a pet basket and hauled him around the island in the boot of the car for eight years. She wanted to leave him in the garden, but he had never been fired. The winter rain would have run him to the ground. Instead, under pressure from her husband, she abandoned him by the village bin, leaving the basket lid open.

Free Spirit
Hazel Buckingham

It's what men dream of, thought Gordon, staring at the whiskey lorry on its side. Whole bottles spun amongst the glistening shards that covered the road and Gordon bent down to collect a "couple".

With two dozen bottles safely secreted, he left the scene before the local constabulary arrived. Once home, he opened a bottle and raised his toasts.

'One for the dead sheep under the lorry, one for the driver, one for the maker, one for me.'

Shame he never read the label: *Contaminated. Do not consume.*

He slumped in his armchair, eyes rolled upwards as his free spirit soared.

Garnish
Arthur Chappell

'Garnish applies to liberal application of body art as well as food-flavour enhancement. A few discreet tattoos enhance the flesh. You have added the body art equivalent of too much salt. I don't find you tasty. You look as if you should be on display in a freak show. Could I meet my next speed-dating contestant now, please?'

Geriatric Star
Darren Wheatley

Weak sunlight created muddy shadows as we stared up into the sky. All across the system, preparations were being made. Some would leave; many would stay. Entropy was spiritual as well as physical. Most would never get used to the idea that the light of their lives would soon be gone. Right now, starting over seemed far too much effort.

Geriatric Star   *Ali Froud*

'It's community singing in the sitting room tonight. Old Mr Bowie in the corner there has promised us a rendition of *Spiders From Mars*. I will be performing my single, *Don't Go Breaking My Heart*, accompanied by dear old Elton. I hope he doesn't try to wear his platform boots again. His hip has only just mended from last time.'

Geriatric Star   *Estelle Kirk*

The geriatric star said 'I do!' and bent forward to be kissed, her green eyelids fluttering like gaudy butterflies. Her face cracked into a smile and powder snowed down onto the lips of her young chauffeur. He clutched her crabbed hand and led her down the aisle. She felt like she was floating. He moved with legs of lead.

Get Me Out of Here   *Alexander Prophet*

The captain stood quietly at the helm, up there, surveying his passengers. Against the wind, his head bobbed loosely on his shoulders, as if attached to a coil of invisible springs, but the action so slow my eyes needed time to adjust. As they did, I withheld myself panicking, for my first thought was, *Oh God, the man is absolutely smashed from the bottle.*

Closer observation made me wiser. There's obviously a terrible illness at work here, probably Alzheimer's, which, however tragic, only enhanced my analysis, for the diagnosis was the same: the man was liable to lose his head.

Get Me Out of Here   *Perry Gretton*

For twenty-eight years, Gary had worked for the same firm. His attendance record had been exemplary. He was, said management, an example to all. Now this: 'Following the company's recent re-organisation . . .'

He had been downsized, reduced to a cipher – an ex-employee.

At the sound of the approaching bus, he stepped off the kerb, eyes closed. He barely heard the squealing tyres.

Get Me Out of Here   *Elizabeth Madden*

I take a deep breath, shrugging my shoulders to ease the tension in my neck. Lactic acid crackles as it diffuses amongst the knots in my muscles. My stomach flutters queasily and I can feel a hot flush creeping up to suffuse my face with red. Heart pounding, pulse racing, I force myself to go into the communal changing room!

Glass   *Perry Gretton*

Over forty years, for one hour of every day, she has presented herself to the three-paned looking glass of her dressing table. Each day, it has reflected what she yearns to see: a face smooth as the glass itself, unblemished, ageless. Today, however, it can no longer conceal the truth. Screaming with rage, she picks up a jar of face cream and hurls it at the glass, which shatters on impact. She throws another jar, and another, and then collapses in tears.

Truth, says Keats, *is beauty, beauty truth*.

But truth is no match for vanity . . . no match at all.

Glass   *Shirley Bunyan*

I was a pilferer of feelings, extracting love from sincerity despite never believing, yet knowing it could get me all I wanted. What I wanted was to be desired, needed and adored.

Reciprocation was unnecessary and emotionally draining. I was very adept at manipulation. I mastered it before it swallowed me. I learned it in the house of grey walls with my mother-dear and father-sir. You think you can melt the coldness that guards me. You dare to recall, with interest, the warmth you touched me with. Yet to melt the ice that glistens like glass would surely drown you.

Gotcha!   *Mark Buchanan*

I swung, a human pendulum, chasing a spotlit silhouette racing across the pitching canvas vault. Ropes creaking, the final swing; I release, somersaulting weightless, a sea of upturned *oohs* below. Outstretched arms rush forward to catch me as the world turns over and over. Reaching out, the approaching hands meet fingertip to fingertip.

'Gotcha!' he grins as the hands quickly withdraw.

Clutching at nothing, I plummet into an abyss of *aahs,* the dirt and straw floor rushing up to meet me.

The crowd gasps as I stop inches from two-dimensional destruction and the ground telescopes away beneath me.

Gotcha!   *Jenni Doherty*

Laughter bounces off the graffiti-scarred tiles. A swiped canteen glass squats upside-down on the bathroom floor. Like an eerie octopus, the girls huddle together in the half-light and silence. Their fingernails shiny as cars: blood-red, silver and neon-pink. Scents mingle into a purring mist of hormones and intense energy. Dry mouths hum like nervous engines.

The glass begins to buzz.

'Shusssh!' someone hisses.

The glass stumbles on G, then O. An alphabet alive, teasing their nerves. It cruises to T. Falters. C. Jerks again . . . H . . . A . . .

'Please, *not* an R!' Charlotte panics to a giggling explode of 'G.O.T.C.H.A!'

Grass   *Amanda Mair*

Have you felt alone? Let down by one you loved, believed in, gave up everything for? Felt things didn't work out how you thought they would?

That's how I felt. I was afraid, not wanting to die or be beaten. So I told them where to find him. I sold out. Reward? Thirty pieces of silver and burning eternity alone.

Grass   *Karen Jones*

'It's not your brother's fault you're in trouble.'

'Is so. He grassed.'

'But you killed it.'

'Didn't mean it.'

'Who fed the pet rat?'

'Me.'

'Who fed it tortilla chips, jalapeños and chocolate ice-cream, washed down with a drink of Vimto?'

'I did.'

'Well?'

'You never said *not* to give it Vimto.'

'It wasn't the . . . Oh, I give up.'

Grass   *Darren Wheatley*

Prising open bleary eyes, I found myself face down on the front lawn, no doubt where I'd come to rest the night before. Alongside me, strewn among the dandelions and dog shit, lay my worldly possessions: CDs, porn, clothes, guitar and, worst of all, my beloved pot plant, ripped into tiny shreds. Guess my brother snitched me up after all.

Green
Lynda Kenny

They've put me in a cell now, with heavy padding on the walls. I know they are worried about me: they keep looking at me through a little window set in the door. I wish I could help them understand. They've been so kind, and I would like them to know exactly why I did what I did. But that is impossible. I am special, you see, so special in fact that they are a little afraid of me. I am sorry about that. I don't mean them any harm, unless I notice the change, and I haven't, not with any of them, not yet, anyway. I am the only one who can see it. That's why I have been chosen. It's quite subtle at first. It's in the eyes, when they become green. I know what I must do. The dead eyes are always their true colour.

Green
Perry Gretton

Kate surveyed the collection on her elder sister's dressing table. Why did Hillary need such expensive cosmetics when she was so beautiful, unlike herself with her dough-like features? It was just unfair.

She picked up a jar of moisturiser, removed the lid and examined the contents. If she were to add sulphuric acid to the cream, would Hillary notice before she applied it? She could filch some easily enough from school.

'What are you doing with that?' Hillary stood in the doorway, hands on hips. 'That's not for the likes of you. Put it down and get out.'

In a flash of fury, Kate hurled the jar at her sister, striking her hard in the face. Hillary staggered back, stunned, blood pouring from her once-perfect nose. And then she screamed. Kate watched her without sympathy or guilt.

Green Fingers *Jenni Doherty*

'So, what are you – taig or hun?'

My hands curl into fierce fists as I answer, on edge, unsure, defensive. Been a long hell of a struggle. Pride. Time to cease, to change, move forward. No more sorry stripes or emblems. No more murder or smear of hate. No more black. We all bleed the same depth, cry the same weight. Red, thick, guilty blood. Sore, bitter, thieving tear. Lost sons, daughters, brothers, sisters . . .

Yes, after this reign of terror, a rainbow coalition of life will grow. Has to.

'Give me your hand, then.'

I let my green fingers embrace orange.

'Peace.'

Green Fingers *Tamzin Mole*

For thirty years, the cactus and its many fat daughters squatted in the small pot in a dusty corner of the windowsill, their spines wreathed in cobwebs.

'I'm glad to get rid of it,' laughed my neighbour. 'Isn't it ugly? Not a single flower.'

My mother brought it home. She teased apart the snare of spines into five new pots. Fed and watered, the hairy shoots grew higher each day.

One evening, the slender buds opened. Above the cactus pots, a crown of crimson flowers floated, satin petals curling, their stamens heavy with enough fragrance to fill a desert sky.

Green Fingers *Gavin Parish*

BREAKING NEWS: The verdict is now in on an ongoing neighbourhood dispute that ended in murder. Max Jacobs, forty-five, was left for dead in a pool of industrial-strength lime-green paint, which he had, moments before, emptied over his neighbour's brand new Ferrari. The prosecution contended that the car's owner, Edward Byrne, sixty-two, was at the wheel when it subsequently ran the victim over. Byrne denied involvement, even though paint was discovered beneath his fingernails. In court, defence counsel Arwel Atkins had the arresting officer's statement ruled inadmissible on the grounds of the misleading phrase, 'We caught him red-handed.'

Green with Envy   *Perry Gretton*

I sat on my mother's bed and watched as she carefully applied unnecessary make-up to her perfect features. When she finished, she came over to me.

'You're such a cutey,' she said, kissing me on my forehead.

In the dressing-table mirror, the purple blotch that covered half my face glared back at me, defiantly challenging her words.

Cutey, eh?

Guilt   *Sarah Star*

Tom still remembered that night in 1917. He'd been lying face down in No-Man's-Land, unable to move, legs spattered by the bullets from an enemy gun. The pain was magnified by the thought that he'd been madly running away whilst his friends were slaughtered. They had followed orders that he'd disobeyed. By pure luck, John had found him and taken him to safety, keeping his secret safe. Now he watched John leave muddy prints across his carpet.

'I need a hundred quid this time, Tom.'

And he knew he would lend it once more. It was the price of living.

Guilt *Colin Biggs*

It was never a simple matter to ignore her sobbing, to feign indifference at her pain and sorrow. It was, however, the only way to give her the guidance that she so desperately needed. I dared not let my actions even suggest that I had any weakness. Such was her latent power that without the cage between us, I knew I would fall, regardless of the lash in my hand. The key that I held became her toy, her weapon to use against me. I traded food and wine for her mercy and respite from her stare. Her hatred grew.

Hair *Teresa Stenson*

He had heard it all his life: 'You look just like your father.'

In the summer, the sun bleached his hair to a yellow that made everyone who had ever known his father stare. Everyone but his mother, who looked at him less and less, until one day she stopped looking at all.

People said things like, 'You might never have known him, Joe, but he's there in you. That hair . . . Jesus. Never known anybody with that hair 'cept him. Bright as anything. You should be proud: he was a great man.' And Joe would smile and hurry away – especially if the sun was out.

But the sun didn't just fade away in autumn and then flick back on in spring. There were days in between when a low and alarming brightness threatened to change him. He learned the routes where shade protected him, zigzagged his way everywhere. He stayed inside at break times, until a teacher found him hiding in the stock cupboard.

When he finally did it, it turned the bath and his ears black as well.

His mother saw him and cried. He let her wash the dye away, then she let him out into the sun.

Hair

Perry Gretton

Laura unclipped the locket from around her neck and passed it to me. Seeing me staring at it uncomprehendingly, she tapped it with a painted fingernail.

'Open it.'

I pressed the catch. Inside lay a coil of fine blond hair.

'Whose is it?' I asked.

'Graham's.'

'Graham?'

'My baby . . . until I gave him up for adoption.'

'Why?'

'I was seriously depressed and there was no-one around to help me look after him.'

'That must have hurt badly.'

'It did. I've never stopped thinking about him.' Her eyes searched mine for a moment. 'He's twenty-three now.'

'Twenty-three? You mean . . .'

'He was born in September nineteen eighty-three. We split up in the previous January. Remember?'

'Of course. So you're saying—'

'There was never anyone else, Peter.'

I sat back, my mind struggling to come to terms with the sudden disclosure.

'Why didn't you tell me?'

'By the time I knew for certain, you were already engaged to Barbara. It didn't seem fair to lay that on you.'

'Perhaps you should have: it would have saved me a divorce. So why tell me now?'

She took the locket from me and gazed at the wisp of hair.

'He's asked to meet his real parents.'

Hair

Sam Robinson

Last week Señora Mafalda Cordóba do Lorenzo triumphed as president of Franciscador after an embittered campaign. Now she lies naked in a morgue, exposed to the pathologist appointed to investigate her death. He is the best, the most reputable in the country.

Her taut waist has never borne a child. Breasts and eyes that caused the deaths of at least two suitors will never again feel or see the blonde hair cascading over her shoulders. As Franciscadorians will tell you, 'Americans think Marilyn Monroe was beautiful only because they never saw Mafalda!'

The doctor undertakes his duties observed by witnesses. Stomach samples reveal nothing. No bruises, no scars, no cuts mar her smooth skin. Her seven orifices reveal no indication of malfeasance. He takes tissue samples for biopsy, working carefully because tomorrow Mafalda must be displayed in an open casket.

Next week, the people will be told she died from poison administered by a person or persons using means unknown. Riots will explode, destroying the capital city and fatally infecting the countryside. Thousands will die, including the assassin who poisoned her with a pin through her thick hair during a congratulatory kiss and who is now performing her autopsy.

Hair

Darren Wheatley

That she was beautiful wasn't the question. It was more about how much better than everyone else she thought that made her. An accident of birth, that's all. Flawless skin bequeathed by a mother lost to cancer. Smouldering black hair bestowed upon her by a rich father who gave her everything else but time. No need to catch her reflection in shop windows; it was in the face of every drooling man, every glaring, green-eyed woman.

If enough people say you're special, you just might believe it. If everyone treats you like a goddess, you might become one. And how the gods love to look down upon mere mortals! Sighing, I watched those perfect hips swing; perfect eyebrows arching condescendingly; perfect feet strapped perfectly into perfect strappy stilettos.

Perfect.

She turned to look in my direction, and that immaculate curtain of ebony swung into the breeze and caught the light just so. Jade-flecked eyes stared directly through the space I occupied and I think she might have actually seen me in the split second before the Number 37 broadsided her.

You know, I don't think she'll look so perfect when I tell her we won't be going upstairs.

Hair   *Hazel Buckingham*

Marcella was pleased when Sydney, her now late husband, started his hobby. He needed something to keep him occupied after forty years as the bank's chief filing clerk. However, his hobby quickly developed into an obsession. Each morning, he paced the hall while waiting for the postman. His smile of anticipation turning to a scowl of malevolence when the letters, once so eager to accept his request, now declined.

Sydney's dying wish was that the collection be destroyed, but Marcella felt the last few years of being cast as second-best justified her selling.

She perched on the edge of the chair as her eyes darted round the room. She knew the glitterati would turn up; they had to – they would not want anyone getting their hands on these items.

'Good afternoon, ladies and gentlemen.' The auctioneer's hand slicked through his oily hair. 'So good to see so many known faces here today.'

Sunglasses lowered and actress smiles chinked their ice against ice.

'Lot number one. What am I bid for this fine collection of pubic hair?'

Every taloned hand raised their baton. The final asking price ensured Marcella a round-the-world cruise and champagne for the rest of her years.

Heavy Burden   *Nicky Philips*

'Sarah, fancy a coffee? I'm off to your workplace at noon to collect my biopsy results immediately they're in.'

'Love one. I'm on late shifts, free till two.'

They coffeed. They talked. They laughed. Madeleine felt so great she decided to join Sarah's gym. Watching her go, Sarah felt the burden of keeping secrets; the results had arrived early.

Heavy Metal   *Tamzin Mole*

The physicians were huddled in the corner of the dying man's chamber, urgently whispering.

'I don't understand. I've tried everything, but he hasn't responded. In fact, he just seems to be getting worse . . .'

They glanced nervously at the patient, whose laboured breaths rasped ever more erratically.

'What have you given him?'

'I've dosed him with mercurial salts, given him antimonial wine sweetened with sugar of lead, and I've bled him twice and purged him all night.'

'And his initial symptoms?'

'Why, it began only as a slight stomach upset.'

The physicians shook their heads despondently.

'It's another mystery,' they agreed.

Heavy Metal   *Hazel Buckingham*

Thump . . . she timed each . . . thump . . . step to the incessant . . . thump . . . beat of her nightmare. Gritting her teeth at the piercing guitar wail, she entered his room – his hallowed shrine to the gods of heavy metal. Black wallpaper, interspersed with hellish visions of sexual deviance, surrounded the gothic-framed bed upon which he rocked, coked out and grinning absurdly.

'Hey, Ma, wassup?' Small rivulets of sweat snaked along the Celtic tattoo on his arm as he waved his faint recognition to his mother.

'This is.'

She raised the club hammer and struck hard, his one scream outlasting the singer's final caustic cacophony.

Heavy Metal   *Darren Wheatley*

Trying hard not to look like a fish out of water, he scanned the crowd for a familiar face. The proximity warning had sounded too late, leaving him stranded amongst the heaving humanity of the busy station platform. As the emergency mission-override subroutines began to clamour for priority, the enhanced pattern-recognition system came to the rescue and, with amazing grace, the android swept through the throng just in time to prevent his charge from stumbling off the platform edge. The child stared uncomprehendingly at his protector and burst into tears. The big droid wasn't equipped to register embarrassment.

Hidden   *Karen Jones*

I watch you close your eyes; your black lashes quiver as sleep takes you in its arms. I watch your chest rise and fall as your breathing deepens, your face smooth in repose, your lips part in silent slumber.

85

I spend each night virtually by your side, catching my breath as if I might disturb you. I watch the languorous movements that accompany your sweet striptease. Sometimes I think you know, that you perform for me . . . but then the light goes out, the one I fitted above your mirror, and you sleep, alone.

I know every inch of your apartment; I know the contents of every drawer, every cupboard. I know you.

Soon, you will know me. Soon, the watching won't be enough. Soon, I'll use my master key and we will meet. I'll wait for you in your bedroom, still hidden, until the light goes out.

Hidden   *Kitty Redding*

The morning voice of the newsreader and the seven o'clock pips wake me. A deep groan and I try to remember the previous evening. Did I know him? His face, contorted. His . . . No. Get up. Go to work.

The bathroom mirror reflects my pale skin accessorised with purple patches. Cotton wool and cleanser removes the dirt, toner stings, moisturiser soothes. Concealer: works like magic. Nearly the whole stick – again.

Foundation makes everything even. A large brush fixes it all with long sweeps of fine powder.

Now for the colour. Eye-shadow, bright. Mascara, black. Blusher, deep rouge and lipstick – two coats.

I drink strong, steaming coffee, black and bitter. It washes down the Paracetamol. I glance at the morning paper: *Veiled Moslem Woman Sacked From School.* How could a woman allow herself to be hidden like that?

In the car, I add a third layer of lipstick.

Hidden   *Nina Simon*

A shadowy figure roams the wastelands of humanity, sleeping during the day, hunting at night. He waits in doorways of derelict buildings, amid broken glass and discarded needles.

From his hiding place, he watches the girls standing by the roadside. They lean against the chain-link fence, shivering in too-short skirts and skimpy crop-tops. A car approaches slowly, headlights blazing.

The girls are distracted. With feral cunning, he moves, homing on his prey. Too easily, he lures her into a dark alley. Pinning her against a wall, his hands explore her body, knead her breasts. A knife glints in the moonlight. Before a scream can escape her lips, her throat is slit. Hungrily he drinks her blood, draining every drop before fleeing into the night.

High Drama *Roy Everitt*

We carried our chairs to the cliff-top theatre for *Romeo and Juliet*. Our romance began here – before the theatre did. He enjoyed the fight scene; I never had. I had always loved "my" balcony scene: *Tis the east, and Juliet is the sun* . . .

Their romance had ended tragically. We left with our chairs: Romeo to his car, me to mine.

High Tide *Eileen Burzynska*

His mates buried him in the sand for fun, his head just poking out.

'Sea monster!' they shouted.

'Water's coming in,' he warned.

The water rushed in.

'God, get me out!'

They started to dig, scrabble, tug, call for help. The water surrounded, pulling, sucking him down. It reached his mouth, his nose, closing over his desperate eyes. So quick . . .

I Remembered
Nathalie Boisard-Beudin

The war was long and nasty. They usually are. Now I stand with my wounds and missing a limb, staring at a wall, reading a roll of names. Comrades and vague shadows, forever lost in the mud of distant fields. Food for poppies. And a name that comes shouting back in my face. My name. And the date I disappeared.

I Wish I Had Been There
Indie Codanda

Dear G

I wish I had been there when your wife died. It must be difficult, knowing how deeply you loved her. I hear you are in bad shape. And that's why I wish I had been there, G. To see you go through what I did when you left our marriage, abruptly and without warning, for her.

Love

S

Identity
Azfarul Islam

He's pale, I'm brown. He's tall, I'm of average height. He enjoys comics, whereas I'll retreat to a good book. He enjoys classical music, I like variety. He excels at pool, whereas I calculate the physics behind it. He loves eating Italian while I'm busy creating my own dishes.

Who am I?

Everything he thinks that I think he isn't.

Identity
Jo Fajer

'You're not tame the way a proper wife should be. You're brash, overconfident, and you talk too loud. You're hot like fire, like a woman who loves sex. Your eyes never stop looking at me.

They watch me like tigers. They make my skin crawl. That's why I have to crush you. And it'll hurt when I do.'

Illusion   *Nina Simon*

He wiped the grimy window with his sleeve. Looking out, he saw her, sitting on the carefully tended lawn, their daughter at her feet, playing happily. She was so beautiful; he ached to hold her, talk to her. Tears prickled his eyes. He turned away. Craving more, he looked again. The garden was a desolate wasteland beside a derelict house.

Illusion   *Anne Rainbow*

'Perception and reality,' said Mrs Jones soberly to her A-level English set. 'Can anyone explain the difference?'

'Perception is what you think?' offered Jimmy, smiling.

'Yes,' said Mrs Jones, imagining Jimmy naked.

'And reality? Anyone else?'

Jenna raised her hand.

'Yes, Jenna?'

'Reality is an illusion brought on by the absence of alcohol, Miss?'

Everyone laughed, and Mrs Jones blushed.

Illusion   *Anatoly Kudryavitsky*

'Friends remain our friends as long as they need us,' an illusion said to a man resentfully and curled up into a cloudlet. Quite similarly, nuts tried to make friends with a squirrel; however, no idyll ever ensued. But the main thing to remember is that an idyll is theoretically possible. Needless to say, we can take comfort from that.

(Translated from the Russian by the author.)

Inconceivable *Arthur Chappell*

'An explanation, Captain. The *Marie Celeste* was floundering. Everyone, including myself, took to her lifeboat, which overturned. I clambered onto an iceberg. I became trapped inside. I should have frozen to death, but it preserved me cryogenically. Tonight, you liberated me by nudging it open with your unsinkable *Titanic* . . . Excuse me, but is the bow supposed to slope like that?'

Inconceivable *Kevin Connolly*

I find her behaviour totally inconceivable. If there's one thing I hate, it's a thief.

She stole everything I owned: my nine FA Cup winner's medals, Bob Monkhouse's joke book, the Irish Crown Jewels, *The Scream* by Edvard Munch, the suit Charlie Chaplin was buried in, and my lovely horse, Shergar. She's even worse than me, the thieving bitch.

Invasion *Darren Wheatley*

First of all, there had been just a few. Huddled and unnoticed in the darkness; feeding, growing, breeding, spreading. By the time they finally came to my attention, they were just as much a part of the natural order as anything that had been there before. Tightly entwined, symbiotic, spreading like wildfire, they began a mass takeover no-one on earth could prevent. In frustration, violent means were resorted to in order to drive them out, but in the end, it was too little, too late.

Cancer.

It's not the dying I mind; it's the waiting that really gets you.

Invasion   *Neil Outram*

A great shadow cast over the city. Mary stopped, looked to the sky, and with wide eyes beheld a UFO the size of London cloaking the afternoon sky. Screams and gasps chorused throughout the streets while she stood in wonderment, lost for words. Then a man barged past her.

'What's going on?' she shouted.

The man, face etched with panic, shouted back: 'Fuck's sake, run!'

Moments later, he was dead: destroyed by a robot carrying an unearthly weapon firing wavy black beams of energy.

Rumours of a new US military weapon had been confirmed with terrifying clarity. Britain was at war.

Invasion   *Jenni Doherty*

Beat her good and proper last night. Slashed his bastard tool between her thighs: thumping, pumped. Ranting rage. Panties torn.

She lay there exposed: raw, bleeding, broken. Numbed inside. Eyes pleading, *please, no*!

Cover the face. Shield the spit. Don't cry. For God's sake, don't whimper. Ten minutes, it's done. Then fast asleep, drunk, forgotten. Be strong. Think of the kids . . . your marriage . . . his family . . . Let him have it. Let it be.

You see, this is how he cares, is showing you his love. Just another Saturday night. No-one will ever know.

'Are you all right there, my love?'

It's a Long Way   *Ali Froud*

The building is imposing. I smile to reassure you. This is the start of our journey to repair our shattered relationship.

'I can't do it. I'm scared, Mum.'

91

I take your hand.

'These are the first steps. It's a long way to where we want to be, but I will walk beside you.'

We enter the drug dependency clinic together.

It Was Green and Had Spots   *Colin Biggs*

There never again was such a summer. Carefree days of picnics, cream teas and chilled champagne on the elegant terrace. Jade made it perfect, occasionally blessing us with her presence, we poor souls, marooned on the estate. I knew my love for her would never end.

Arriving one evening, she flowed out of the car, an auburn cascade, enlivening the house, enchanting the Masters.

Her green dress, daring yet discreet, clung to her slender body, the perspiration running down her skin, making dark spots spread across the woven silk. She coughed quietly, and I knew that she would not see winter.

It Was Green and Had Spots   *Sarah Star*

I made a dinosaur at school. I painted it green with purple spots and called him Norman.

'No!' said the teacher. 'Dinosaurs are brown. They have names which end in -saurus.'

'How do you know?' I asked.

'I have years of study of the subject,' said my teacher. 'And you are only a small girl who knows nothing.'

He made me paint him beige and call him Tyrannosaurus Rex.

I looked at Tyrannosaurus Rex. He looked at me. We knew that, underneath, he was really green with purple spots. Tyrannosaurus Rex was just his surname. His friends called him Norman.

It Was Late *Darren Wheatley*

Phil stared at the blinking green numerals as they ticked off the story of another day gone by. This was the fourth time this week, ever since she'd started her new job. His head pulsed with images unbidden. He'd believed he'd be stronger than this, but it was all too much to take.

Maybe pimping wasn't for him, he thought.

It Was Late *Mark Buchanan*

He knew he ought to leave but had never tried Fugu and wasn't going to waste it. The others had already gone to the conference room for the meeting. Initially, he thought it was the Sake when his hands and feet started tingling. Sweating profusely, his arms and legs refusing to cooperate, he could only wink frantically at the waiter.

It Was So Foggy *Roy Everitt*

The siren sounded a sonorous tone through the blackness, distantly audible above the gently slapping waves. He edged onwards, pulling against the oars . . .

Now he heard the rocks close by, breasting the sea's insistent swell either side of him.

Behind him, then, must be the soft sandy beach which lay between – where his siren called and waited, called and waited.

It Was So Foggy *Lynda Kenny*

'How'll we make it to Skeleton's Cove, Cap'n?' the mate asked.

'Ne'er worry,' the reply. 'My fair Mary will lead us in to the cove with a light.'

'But, Cap'n, the treasure?'

Mary went down the secret steps, and the light o' the lantern spilled, fractured and made gold of the cave walls. Turning her back, she blew out the flame.

Junk Mail   *Calvin Lord*

On my carpet, *Readers Digest* in Verdana on an envelope's face. It had been filled with care for someone who didn't. The cost of this unsolicited chance for riches? The daily income of a street child in Rio.

I trashed it like all of its brethren.

If I'd known, would I have looked at its contents?

NO.

Junk Mail   *Roy Everitt*

It was as he was being hoisted onto the horse that he chose to make his complaint.

'It cramps me terribly, and some of these edges are really very sharp. A knight could do great self-harm wearing this.'

'Indeed, sire. So what shall I say to the armourer?'

'Tell him,' he said, wincing, 'tell him this is junk mail.'

Just One More   *Perry Gretton*

'Just one more,' said Miriam, helping herself to a cream cake.

George wondered how long her arteries could withstand the assault.

'Have the last one,' he offered.

'Oh, all right, then.' She filled her mouth with an éclair. 'Delicious,' she mumbled.

'By the way, I also bought a Swiss roll today.'

'Oh, you adorable man.'

'I'll get it for you, dear.'

Just One More *Robert Capps*

Photographable? Yes, certainly it was. Strangely, this phosphorescent glow also shimmied in tune with the shivers shaking Rupert's body. He tried opening and shutting his eyes, chanting mantras, calling to the gods he never believed in, yet still it was there. Too many questions unanswered, like – why was he carrying a scythe? Swallowing several more tablets, he awaited death's answers.

Just One More *Shirley Bunyan*

The excitement was unbearable. After twenty-five years, just once more would Peter endure this detestable journey. He remembered the day he'd decided.

It was the weathervane that clinched it. He closed his eyes, lulled by the sleepy rhythm of the train, picturing it twisting . . . turning . . . slowly on a summer breeze. Soon . . . soon . . .

He never saw the tree across the track.

Keeping Faith *Lee Henderson*

'Hey, Arsehole! Yeah, you, stupid! Get over here.'

Coaches have a way with words.

'Who the hell do you think you are? Babe Ruth? I told you before the game, Knucklehead – keep it tight, keep it compact. When I say go, you fucking go! Okay, Wonder Boy? Keep faith with me, boy, and we win.'

I did – and we won.

Keeping Faith *Arthur Chappell*

Lord Torquemada

Bloodstains in the torture chambers can be slippery. Please clean them up immediately. Rack levers need oiling to prevent back-injury for the operator. Overuse of thumbscrews can cause arthritis for elderly torturers. Auto-da-fé heresy fires need better crowd control so none of the faithful spectators get burnt, too.

Yours sincerely

The Spanish Inquisition Health & Safety Executive

Lady Godiva's Room   *Annie Bien*

'Please, come in. I once owned stitched and cut garments, but now I only have textured fabrics for furniture. Velvets so soft, silks, satins, no corsets, no upholstery. Mostly, I need nothing more in my room than my hair. Let me help you undress. I don't consider myself a modernist, but an elemental woman. I toss my hair out the window like Rapunzel, for sustenance, my urn and washbasin full with water for cleansing and drinking. Air to breathe, logs blaze near our nakedness for warmth. My modesty depends upon your eyes only, not mine. Stay, if you like.'

Lady Godiva's Room   *Kitty Redding*

Watching her reflection, she removed her cloak, sliding it from her shoulders, allowing it to slip to the ground. She waved away help. The maids gasped. Her dress was next. Unbuttoning, top to bottom, over her breasts; down to her navel, beyond. Under-garments spilling out once freed from their binding.

They gazed, silent, captivated. Her delicate fingers eased the laces down her back, pulling them apart, freeing her. Golden hair let loose. Her milk-white body, slender, young, shivered in the cold morning air.

'It's time,' she said.

They curtseyed, cheeks blazing. Lady Godiva opened her chamber door and stepped out.

Last Chance   *Maureen Wilkinson*

The river slapped at her face like a wet hand; foam snapped and cracked about her ears. The sharp edges of the rock she clung to bruised her skin as she buffeted against it. Her strength was ebbing as she awaited his return with help. *That had been her last chance*, she thought as she slipped silently out to sea.

Last Chance   *Perry Gretton*

Saint Peter looked up from his massive ledger.

'My, you have been a naughty boy, haven't you?'

Saddam nodded meekly.

'I really ought to send you straight to hell.'

'No, please, don't do that. I want to go to Paradise.'

'Mmm . . . maybe. But only on one condition.'

'What's that?'

'You tell us where you hid those weapons of mass destruction . . .'

Late Again   *Sabrina Fatma Ahmad*

The coffeehouse was crowded when I entered and wrangled for myself a corner table. There were faces all around me; smiles, tears, frowns. Where were you?

Three cold cups of coffee later, I knew you weren't coming. Paying the bill, I left, fighting my tears, cursing myself for ever having read your text message asking me to meet you . . . tomorrow?

Late Again   *Heidrun Knikander*

The potatoes are cooked to mush. The meat is cooling down in the oven. The salad is withering. Tears are besmeared over her face. She couldn't reach him. In her imagination, she is expecting the worst. Why didn't he call? Did he have an accident? Is he in the hospital?

A key turns in the lock; he is late again.

Liar

Eileen Burzynska

It's not what you think at all. I can't imagine how we ended up in that position. She was just resting on the sofa when she thought she felt a button digging into her, so I was feeling under the back cushions. Then I thought I'd better check it was not one of my fly buttons. Then you came in.

Liar

Darren Wheatley

'This might be my last chance, Laura. I'm leaving soon, so let me take you to the dance.'

'How many times? I'm not going . . . what do you mean "last chance"?'

'Bone cancer: only six months to live. I can go into deep freeze until a cure is found, but that could take years.'

'Well, since you put it like that . . .'

Like a Charm

Lynda Kenny

The gypsy pulled herself up the single step into her caravan. Breathing heavily, limbs aching, she sank into her chair with a sigh. From here, she surveyed her little room, a place filled with a lifetime's worth of memories, silks, wall hangings and her crystal ball. She knew her time had come. Rising again, she boiled a kettle and removed some leaves from the little plant on the table.

Barefoot and bejewelled, the girl ran to meet the tribe elder, a man in his early twenties.

'My Anya,' he smiled. 'It worked again.'

'Like a charm,' she replied, black eyes dancing.

Like a Charm   *Alexander Prophet*

Every meal has a story: seduction, anger, murder, laziness, arrogance, diplomacy, hunger, betrayal, to name but a few. Seduction is my personal favourite, the one I'll be serving tonight to Stephanie.

I'll start with Corsican goat-cheese, Spanish olives and stuffed peppers, dried tomatoes in olive oil and fresh herbs, and a nice French wine. That'll soften her up for the main course: my magic lamb curry. And for dessert, coconut ice-cream with marshmallows and nuts, topped with vanilla yoghurt and chocolate bits. A wonderful and reliable dessert; works likes a charm.

What else is missing? Yes, candles, and fresh bread.

Like a Charm   *Jenni Doherty*

A sinister moon hung like a suicide's scream over the deadly heat of a thousand lustful sins and secrets. Tonight, she would charm again.

She wore a blood-red coral bracelet of seven beads, signifying the seven deadly sins. By sunrise, she will have destroyed one man, one sin from the chain.

Strangers had fallen in love with her. She'd lure them deep to her seductive curse. Their sexual greed was her salvation; a total surrender with no remorse. But why should she suffer alone? They had infected her.

Now she would give them back a little.

Call it Gift Aid.

Little Pleasures   *Jill Paiton*

The bailiffs would be here soon. Pearl's possessions were never hers for long. Since her Stan's death, she had been considered a liability by her family and friends.

One frequent companion gave her existence meaning – the sounds and lights of the jackpot emanating from her favourite machine.

However, lately, Pearl had found, even that little pleasure was becoming less reciprocal.

Lock and Key   *Gavin Parish*

Hillary pushed the torn-off strip of newspaper under the door and expeditiously jiggled her hairpin inside the lock until the key came loose on the other side. She held her breath; the moment of truth. Success! She pulled newspaper and key through the gap just as footsteps approached on the other side.

'Where's the damn key?'

A fist beat on the door, but the wood was too tough. The man went away again. Clutching the cellar key in her small trembling hand, she would not risk using it now; only later when – sobered up – Daddy had left for work.

Lock and Key   *Colin Biggs*

The car stopped. Suddenly, the key she wore around her neck burned against her skin.

Black windows – boarded, broken – stared, cold and empty. There, at the top of the house, the view of the attic room that she remembered, just the same as she had seen when driving away, wrapped warm in the shiny blanket and caring arms. Seventeen years, passed from house to home to house again. Never yet had she felt as safe as there in the attic room. Daddy never hurt her, just himself. The scars she carried were payment for watching him die outside her cage.

Low Tide
Roy Everitt

'I'm at a low tide.'

'You mean low ebb.'

'Low, anyway.'

'I know, Mum. You've been unwell, but once you get through today . . .'

'Not sure I can. Not again.'

'Dad would have wanted you to have a life. To carry on.'

'Yes, he always said . . .'

'Anyway, it's time.'

We paused in the church doorway. Her new groom turned and smiled.

Low Tide
Lynda Kenny

Just before dawn and the ship was caught on a sand bank, time running out. The console winked and flashed as the thrusters struggled to break her free. Suddenly she was, and the silver, saucer-shaped ship slid beneath the water before the Upper Crust dwellers had risen.

Magnolia
Colin Biggs

With months of detailed scheming finalised, the project could begin. The promised typhoon rumbled distantly as the early Star ferry rolled across the harbour into Central.

Jostled and uncomfortable, Fothergill grasped the portfolio ever more tightly, knuckles whitened, palms sweating, avoiding every stare. He contemplated the day's first meeting – an introduction to Golden Fortune, Schenzen's largest shipping company.

A drink was needed first – Mama's House, downtown Wan Chai, a twenty-four-hour haven. The bar was empty – except for Magnolia. As she smiled at him, pouring the first drink, he knew that, once again, he would fail to keep the appointment.

Magnolia

Karen Jones

'I love your new house.'

'Thanks. Would you like the guided tour?'

'Oh, yeah. I love a good nosey.'

'Okay, this is the living room – we went for creams and browns in here – very comforting, relaxing colours.'

'Lovely.'

'This is the bathroom – blue to conjure up images of the sea – and it's a calming colour, too.'

'Beautiful.'

'Kids' room – green – their favourite football team's colours.'

'Boys and their football, eh?'

'Kitchen – we went for orange and lemon – vibrant colours to reflect our love of spicy food.'

'Oh, it's so bright!'

'And finally, the master bedroom.'

'Magnolia?'

'Yep.'

'Oh, I'm so sorry.'

Magnolia

Darren Wheatley

The estate agent was due any minute and the paint hadn't yet dried. Brushes, rollers, sponges – I'd tried the lot. I'd never been a fan of DIY, preferring to let Judy roll her sleeves up. After all, it was always her idea. Most of the time, the paint smell just made me sick.

'Ah, magnolia. It'll need redoing, of course.'

You could tell they weren't interested; even the estate agent's patter was lacklustre. As I showed them the door, still mumbling platitudes, my gaze swept quickly to the corner of the front room. There, the drops of burgundy still showed.

Make-Up *Amy Rafferty*

Her neglected son has finally managed to make her notice. Stunned, she takes in his new look. Platinum wig, make-up and delicate lace lingerie.

'What do you think?' he asks. He would do anything for his mother's attention.

She looks and says, 'Nice. But that's maybe not the right colour of lippy for you, son. Maybe try your dad's.'

Memento *Lynda Kenny*

Solomon took Mekeda by the hand and led her through the secret chambers. Touching an outcrop in the rock, one section of the wall opened unto a cave of such proportions that Mekeda thought it might go on forever. This vault contained vast quantities of gold and jewels; in truth, there was so much gold that its reflection made her dark skin glow the colour of bronze. She had travelled across desert lands and the Red Sea to meet this king, famed through the known world for his wisdom and wealth. She had taken to him many gifts, the weight of four elephants in gold and precious stones, an abundance of exotic spices and a vast array of silks. She had stood before him as a queen, his equal. In their time together, he had told her the secrets of his kingdom and the truth of his heart. He had loved her and gave her all that she desired.

Twenty years had passed, and in her own land of Sheba, Mekeda watched her son, Menelik, prepare for the journey that would bring him to the land of his father for the first time. His mother had tutored him greatly on what he would see and the customs to be observed.

She had instructed him also to bring to her a memento of his journey. To this end, eight slaves were made blind and mute; to them would fall the task of carrying the object. For all the wealth that Solomon possessed, there was one thing more precious to him than all – and, she suspected, was the very source – of his power and wisdom.

Her son would steal for her the Ark of the Covenant.

Mind Games   *Karen Jones*

They were gaining on her. She hid, silent, watchful. The adrenalin rush of the chase had been replaced by fatigue. The pain from the bullet that had slammed into her leg made her nauseous, a relentless reminder of her failure. She took out her knife, clenched her teeth, then sliced through the flesh around the wound. She slid into darkness.

She awoke to find her enemies standing in the puddle of her blood, their guns and grins levelled at her face. The calming voice whispered in her headphones, 'Thank you for playing virtual mind games. I'm sorry – you lose.'

Mind Games   *Colin Biggs*

'Welcome, Geraldine Seventy-Two, proceed to Recreation Pod fourteen.'

Wearily, Geri took the token proffered by the Mek and mounted the conveyor.

'We are pleased to inform you, Geraldine Seventy-Two, that this is your final recreational activity period.'

'Really! Why's that?'

'Our Leader Twenty-Three has agreed to integrate recreational programming within the work module. Unproductive recreational sessions are thus unnecessary.'

'What about physical interaction?'

'No longer required. Synthetic synaptic response will be upgraded.'

As she greased her sweating nineteen stone into the pod,

Geri peered at the pallid folds of barely male flesh quivering in Pod fifteen.

'Thank Org for that,' she whispered.

Mind Games   *Darren Wheatley*

The Consortium has this thing down pat; they make it sound so simple. It all comes down to triggering the hindbrain. I just read these few words, pause in the right places, smile when I should, frown when it's needed. Maybe I'll add a little of that good-ol'-country-boy charm, just to be sure. All my life, I've planned, sacrificed, manoeuvred and clawed my way up just to be here for this one sweet moment. All I have to do now is keep them happy. They'll be watching tonight, for sure. Well, here goes nothin'.

'My fellow Americans . . .'

Mind Games   *Richard Chalu*

'What are you?'

'A slut.'

'Remove your dress.'

She complied. It slithered down her smooth body and crumpled around her feet. He walked around her like a sergeant on kit inspection. He paused to unclip her bra. As he brushed the straps from her shoulders, the delicate cups rested briefly on her youthful breasts before falling to the floor. The morning sun, diffused by blinds, flecked her body with warm colours. He unclipped his belt, then the camcorder lens cap.

'Meet Jed.'

A brutish looking hulk appeared from nowhere. The hypnotist smiled – the New Modelling Agency adverts were yielding richly.

Missing Link *Corey Evans*

Grandmother had lost her locket in Paris.

Colombine found the tattered letters and an old photograph in Mami's trunk, which led her here, beneath the Arc de Triomphe.

Mami looked so young, Papi holding her, posing on the same steps Colombine descended fifty years later. The locket was clearly visible in the faded photograph.

She kicked away some Coke cans and crumpled Gitanes packs to reveal a small sewer grate at the base of the stairs. Bending down, she caught a glimmer of gold under the grate. Sure enough, it was Mami's locket, intact except for the light gold chain.

Missing Link *Gavin Parish*

'It's a school project,' Heidi explained keenly. 'A family tree.'

Her grandmother looked sad. 'I never knew my parents. The war made orphans of many children.'

Heidi felt guilty now for asking. Her grandmother had a distant look in her eye. She slipped away and left the old woman alone with her memories.

After Heidi had gone, her grandmother opened her locket and wept. One of the portraits was conspicuous by its absence. The other, a woman she could bear no malice to, who had died almost sixty years to the day in a bunker beneath the streets of Berlin.

Missed Opportunity *Shirley Bunyan*

I could have told him today; explained how sick I am of this so-called relationship. I could have laid down the law about his couch-potato ways and how weary I am of dreary days and passionless nights. I could even have told him about my three-month-old affair. I could have told him . . . if only he hadn't said it first.

Missed Opportunity   *Eileen Burzynska*

Her mother sang exquisitely, so she didn't sing at all. She was a good teacher, so that was out. Her mother travelled and spoke foreign languages well, so she studied xenophobia and excelled. Her mother was religious, so she was an atheist.

'You are not a bit like me, are you?' said her mother regret-fully.

'Thank God,' she answered bitterly.

Miss Willmott's Ghost   *Karen Jones*

She seems so ethereal. He watches her glide around the school-room, so softly, soundlessly, delicately. Her long, thick dark hair accentuates the pale perfection of her complexion. Her dress is as fine and fitted as a second, silken, shimmering skin. She never seems to see him, walks through him, causes him to shiver as they briefly merge as one. A union of bodies he had always dreamed of – but not like this. She is as oblivious to his presence in death as she was in life.

He was Miss Willmott's besotted pupil; now he is Miss Will-mott's devoted ghost.

Moon Dancing   *Roy Everitt*

He had done this since their first year together.

Rowing steadily towards the middle of the vast lake until the moon appeared above the pine-topped hills and its reflec-tion shone clearly on the icy water, he stood and dived in. The moon danced briefly upon the ripples and shimmered dimly from below.

And again, he did not find her.

Moon Dancing *Julieann Campbell*

The warming rain tingled as it cascaded over their writhing, moonlit bodies. Captured by the moment, a thousand miles from home, good old-fashioned rock 'n' roll had rekindled their soul.

Liberated, they danced along the beach and in the surf, thrilled to be alive. Enchanted, they danced away their worries and their woes – danced away their disapproving grandchildren.

Moon Dancing *Lynda Kenny*

The Worshippers of the sun danced around the girl. Wearing long-snouted masks, they turned and dipped and twisted as one. The terrified young girl, suspended over a pool of water, struggled desperately against the thongs that bound her. Suddenly, they stopped, lifted their spears and struck. As the moon's reflection bled, they were sure the sun would rise again.

More or Less *Karen Jones*

She dressed for their "reconciliation" date. Typical of him, giving it a special title.

Even the cause of their break up had been named: "Marsha's little madness". Her "little madness" was the only thing that kept her sane.

He had questioned her in that calm, considered way of his. She had responded in kind: it was a one-night stand; she had been drunk; she was sorry. She omitted to mention that the "one night" was every Tuesday.

She promised him it would never happen again. She'd changed her lover's day to Wednesday, so it was true – more or less.

More or Less *Teresa Stenson*

I'm burying you. I'm about to sprinkle the dirt, but have paused. You're looking at me.

'I've stopped,' you gasp through pale, dry lips.

'You're lying. Have you?'

'More or less.'

I want to believe you, but I'm so used to your lies. I look a little closer.

I never expected you to flicker. Something is switched on again inside of me. A thing I have let die; sent away with you.

'Not yet,' you say.

But I need more than a "more or less", so I let my light go out and push my fingers back into the earth.

More or Less *Teri Davis-Rouvelas*

Baskin understood his mother's concerns: she only had his best interests at heart.

'Why don't women see what I can see in you?' she asked. He smiled as he tucked her bedclothes around her paralysed legs. 'Really, Baskin, at your age, don't you think you should just give it up?'

'More or less,' he replied. 'We'll see.'

Later, sipping some oatmeal stout, he pondered her questions. Maybe it was time to stop hunting for Mrs Right. After all, if he hadn't found her after years of careful searching . . .

Besides, there were those disappointing odours emanating from the cellar.

Moving Picture *Darren Wheatley*

John stared at the clean patch of wallpaper, surrounded by the dirt of half a century. He was sure there had been a picture there the day before. Recalling the wake, he tutted as he imagined one of the mourners helping themselves to a "keepsake" that would probably fetch a pretty penny in the salerooms.

Returning to his flat, John glanced up at the mantelpiece and was unsurprised to see a small portrait of his Gran hanging there, smiling serenely, a tear glistening in the corner of her eye.

He stood quietly until the tears ran down his face, too.

Moving Picture   *Estelle Kirk*

The old lady in the rocking chair looked through the window towards the sea. She had watched the mesmeric aqua peaks and salt spray for many years. But now her niece was moving. She survived the journey on the train. My, how people had changed! She saw couples kissing in public, a man pick his nose and women with their knickers on show. But at last they arrived. There was a lovely view from the lounge into the park. She remembered once, many years ago, strolling there arm-in-arm with a sailor. She smiled as she gazed out of her frame.

National Emergency   *Darren Anderson*

So, due to an administrative error in the processing department of the afterlife, the dead returned, slouching towards the tollbooths. Soon, they were appearing on talk shows and the postlife look was all the rage on the catwalks. Contrary to popular belief, there were no flesh-eating ones. They just came back as they had left. Some went back to work.

Neighbourhood Watch   *Darren Wheatley*

I've been on the Watch now for a month and so far it's been all action. Why, it was only last week the bin men scratched the

Colonel's car and would've got away scot-free if it wasn't for the old Luger I keep in the magazine rack. People used to say I took the job too seriously. Not anymore.

Neighbourhood Watch *Eileen Burzynska*

Last week, I was watching Mr Salah.

In and out of his house he went, seven times on Friday. Last time, comes back with a big parcel. Well, you can't be too careful these days, so I phoned the police and they were round, questioning, everyone out in the street looking scared stiff.

So this week, I'm watching Mr Aziz.

New Age *Liz Gallagher*

He was sceptical about claims of instant healing. In his eighties, he had always had knee pain. This intensified since a lady on the Number 16 bus tripped and fell over him. The instant healer asked him to walk across the stage, swinging both arms. He did so, claiming his resemblance to a Russian soldier. He did this four times. The tension was palpable. The instant healer told him to push his lower pelvic area forwards and backwards. He did so, rhythmically, several times. The audience gasped. The elderly gentleman said his wife would be pleased and returned to his seat.

New Age *Darren Wheatley*

After six weeks in bandages, Vanessa was tired of looking like a mummy, bored of staring at the same four walls and literally itching to unwind.

Doctor Ronaldo welcomed her into his outpatients' clinic and began right away to unwrap his latest masterwork. The tension mounted as the heap of discarded gauze rose in sympathy

111

until, at last, the final length dropped to the ground along with fifteen years of suntans, harsh stares and too much make-up.

A different Vanessa stared back from the mirror, twenty-five again and yet, somehow, not. Physical scars may heal, but life cannot be unlived.

Next, Please! *Calvin Lord*

My wife booked me into Déjà Vu for a haircut. Cropped tops and stretch marks. Orange-wrinkled parchment skin. Oestrogen implants. Sockets painted gold. Plaster Romanesque pillars with supporting cast of busts. Comparison of where tans ended and pubes began. Hair wrapped in silver foil and violent colours. Slight smirk as I entered. Never again – except for a bet!

Next, Please! *Mark Buchanan*

Just popped in for a quick shave next to the pie shop, sat down and waited a short while. I was the last customer.

'Next, please,' he called. I sat in the chair and put my head back as he foamed my face. A slight sting, then the hot lather running down my neck. So relaxing; I soon fell asleep.

Next, Please! *Ali Froud*

Nearly his turn. Rob felt sick, sweaty. He had thought it through, but what would Amy say when she found out? The pictures on the waiting-room walls and the smell of antiseptic nearly made him change his mind and flee.

'Next, please.'

Later, a text message.

'Can't see you anymore. Sorry – Amy.'

The "Rob/Amy" tattoo on his arm throbbed.

Night Moves   *Perry Gretton*

'Henry, wake up! I heard noises downstairs.'

Not again. Kathy, his young wife, had an overactive imagination and he was getting too old for nocturnal adventures.

'Henry!'

He crept out onto the landing, Kathy not far behind. The next moment, he was hurtling headfirst down the long flight of stairs. She waited for a while before going back to bed.

Night Moves   *Shirley Bunyan*

The blade felt hard and cold against her throat as she watched her own terrified eyes in its cold reflection.

'Deadline – eight o'clock tomorrow morning,' he rasped through yellowing teeth. 'Yer brats'll get it first, then you.'

Her head cracked against the bottom banister as he shoved her viciously before he disappeared.

'Wake up, Tommy, Charlie. Hurry, we have to leave . . . tonight.'

No Memory   *Eileen Burzynska*

'Who are you, dear? So kind of you to come and see me. What do we do now? You come in? We have a nice cup of tea? You make it – I see. I haven't seen you for a long time. Last Thursday, was it? It seems like yesterday. Who are you, dear? I don't remember. I have a "forgettery".'

No Memory   *Darren Wheatley*

Lying here coddled and probed by a bleeping cloud of machinery, I am clothed in antiseptic anonymity. *Tabula rasa*: the proverbial blank slate. If we are the sum of our memories, then I am truly no-one. Starched nurses bustle and fuss, their painted smiles yet another part of the treatment. If only I knew what I'd been running from.

No Rehearsal   *Jenni Doherty*

Her face sears, a mask of hot prickles, when people stare. Unseeing strangers. The quiet makes her shiver. She has a sense of herself, twinkling, in that cluster of hushed seconds. Silver screen swells with colour, pulses, hurls light. Upturned faces licked by ghostly beams. Whispers simmer with back-seat parties as secret sensations rise.

There he is: a creature struck stupid by torch-wink. An awesome eye, face whacked angelic with light. Above the shimmer of lips, her eyes sting, stunned. Can he see her?

Everyone folds back into velvet; squirming laughter, creasing faces, oblivious.

First date – no rehearsal.

Nothing On   *Shirley Bunyan*

Margaret grimaced at the noise emanating from the bathroom. *Why did he imagine he turned into Tom Jones every time he showered?* she wondered.

'So, are you coming or not?' she squealed, trying to be heard above the din.

'No, dear. Just singing.'

'Don't be facetious. I need a definite answer.'

'Oh, all right, then, dearest. Seeing as I've nothing on.'

Nothing On   *Indie Codanda*

She had nothing on him, yet she couldn't get over the niggling feeling that he was cheating. It took six months for her to work ceaselessly into shape, her figure once again like in college. But he hadn't noticed at all. Finally, that night, she had evidence: he ignored her when she strutted past with nothing on. So she left.

Now or Never
Robert Capps

Reggie really needed to lose weight fast. About twelve stone would do . . . give or take a few pounds. Reggie was not that fat. Or suffering with weak knee joints. He had stepped over the edge of the Grand Canyon only six seconds ago. The ground was approaching fast. If he became as light as a feather, he'd live.

Now or Never
Jenni Doherty

Whitewashed buildings, with small blue-shuttered windows, stunned streets, steeped like staircases. A honeycombed maze led through low arches to blind, hidden corners, where marauding Turkish pirates once had boiling oil poured on their heads. A world of its own, a life folded in on itself, a clenched stone fist.

It was then that he asked her, 'Will you marry me?'

Now or Never
Eileen Burzynska

I am trembling and sick, arms heavy and useless, fingers prickling with pins and needles. My mind has gone completely blank and stars cascade in front of my eyes. This is a horrifying dream. Please, God, let me wake up. This is it now. Force the legs to move forward and smile at all the faces and start to sing.

Occupational Hazard
Karen Jones

In another era the general would have used binoculars, but today he is seated safely in the situation room, watching pictures sent via satellite link.

'Send them in,' he says, savouring the familiar rush of power.

'Shouldn't we wait for reinforcements? They'll be there—'

'Send them in!' he commands.

The control he wields is as remote as his retreating conscience.

Occupational Hazard   *Darren Wheatley*

She told me something that first night. 'It's just a job, love. Never take any of it seriously. Some people have needs; we fulfil them. They ask. You perform. They pay. Don't bring anything of yourself in; don't take anything away.'

I'm looking at my son, all pink and crinkly. Ten tiny fingers, ten tiny toes. Occupational hazard, I guess.

Occupational Hazard   *Azfarul Islam*

'You missed that turn!' the nasal voice breathed into his ear again. 'Oh, another one.' This time a little more high-pitched. He was enjoying it, the bastard. 'You'll fail, you know,' he said, feigning solemnity, the snigger all too obvious.

Clenching his teeth, Faiyaz pressed hard on the accelerator, crashed into the wall and turned off his PlayStation 2.

Occupational Hazard   *Jenni Doherty*

Oscar was so looking forward to the Sea Monsters' Saint Patrick's Day Ball. He had been practising for weeks but in his rush to get dressed he had forgotten his violin. He knew what would happen next. He'd be put on percussion and he hated that stupid xylophone.

'Damn these octopus tentacles,' he scowled. 'I may as well get legless . . .'

Occupational Hazard   *Arthur Chappell*

'You're no necromancer but you summoned me. How?'

'I'm an antiquarian. I found a book penned in an unknown language. I put it through my computer scanner software and read out the words phonetically. I didn't know what they meant. Honest. Oh God, I just sent the same summons out on the Internet.'

'I'll soon have more souls to feed on, then . . .'

Occupational Hazard   *Carolyn Roberts*

'Ow! Oh, it really hurts. I can't even hold my glass of gin, my wrist is so painful.'

'Oh, you've done it again, have you? Well, if you will go round shaking hands with every blithering idiot that shoves themselves in front of you, what do you expect?'

'Philip, you really are very unsympathetic . . . And you're sitting on my corgi!'

On Something   *Perry Gretton*

A key performance indicator for Brigadier Collins was the total deaths of soldiers under his command, which this month had reached 127, exceeding his limit of 100. Something needed to be done quickly.

'Major.'

'Sir?'

'We need to redefine death.'

'How about "no vital signs for two weeks", sir?'

'I think you're on to something. What's the new figure?'

'Fifty-seven.'

'Excellent!'

117

Organism Friday
Mark Buchanan

An electromagnetic fossil footstep marches through the static, spattered strata of space and time to deliver a cosmic claxon call. Through wormholes and time inversions, it ends its journey at the focal point of a vast parabolic dish. The ancient extraterrestrial signal is subject to much public interest and speculation.

Mathematicians and cryptologists spend months analysing and deciphering the complex parallel bit streams. Eventually, a stable coherent video image forms on the monitors. At first, it seems there is a mistake in the wiring, but slowly it dawns on the stunned researchers: there are no cameras pointed directly at them.

Party
Eileen Burzynska

Bright light, slightly nervous, clean room, eats out, bottles full. Bell rings. Hi, darling. Hey, there, glad you could come; have a drink. Voices buzz, music throbs, singing, screeching, milling, dancing, lurching. Lights low, subsiding on chairs, floors, beds. Food gone, bottles empty, door open. Bright light, slightly dazed, wrecked room, everyone gone. One collapsed in the corner. There always is.

Passion
Karen Jones

'So, what was it like?'

'Sore, a bit messy, but good – dead passionate.'

'Are you and him going together now?'

'Of course we are!'

'I only asked. I hope he used a condom.'

'Nah, he doesn't like them.'

'But you'll get pregnant!'

'No – he used the withdrawal method.'

'What's that?'

'So long as he leaves right afterwards, everything is okay.'

Passion   *Elizabeth Madden*

And God said, 'It's all fixed. Judas betrays you, the Romans crucify you—'

Jesus interrupted. 'I thought you told me I was going to live forever? If I die now, it'll all be finished, just when people were starting to believe me.'

'Don't be silly, lad! They'll be talking about you for centuries after this. Just think of all the religious wars that will be fought in your name, all the bloodshed, the martyrdom. The movie will be fantastic!'

Passion   *Lynda Day Martin*

Sliding his cloven hoof toward her, he said negligently, 'You, like others of your kind, are only good when there's no-one with whom you want to be bad.'

Under the table, her left foot knew what her right one soon would: the hidden pressure of his calfskin.

She stabbed at her sliced tomato. Her prayer flew beating against the chandelier.

Pieces of Me   *Darren Wheatley*

I saw the advert on a message board. Sickened, but intrigued, I replied and arranged to meet. Caught by the strange light in his eyes, we plotted over beer and bratwurst. Somehow, I abandoned myself to his compulsion. The feeling was electric. Waiting expectantly, as tiny morsels pop and spit in the pan. Immortality assured, warm feelings suffuse my damaged skin.

119

Pieces of Me   *Eileen Burzynska*

I have a depressing notion that all our loftiest ambitions and craziest dreams, our fondest memories and worst nightmares, all our accumulated erudition and acquired wisdom, our highest accolades and proudest achievements, are ultimately as ephemeral and expendable as the detritus abandoned on the bedroom, bathroom and barbershop floor: a few flakes of skin, strands of hair and nail clippings.

Please Put My Leg Down   *Ali Froud*

It was a fantastic dinner. I felt sexy in my miniskirt and long boots. Electricity crackled as we whispered secret fantasies across the cheesecake. Afterwards, a nightcap at our local.

'I love your boots,' squealed Annie and lifted my leg for a closer look. The bloke opposite nearly got a full eyeful.

'Please put my leg down,' I hissed.

Please Put My Leg Down   *Darren Wheatley*

'I realise that you have a need to show off and maybe you think you're hilarious. Let me tell you, I'm a long way from laughing right now. Okay, joke over; I need that to get home. It's not a toy, you're not big, and I'm not impressed with your Jake the Peg impersonation. Now, please put my leg down.'

Please Put My Leg Down   *Mark Buchanan*

She's beautiful, does the splits and moves well. Her foot's on my shoulder and I'm fully standing. I place my hand under her foot and raise it higher. Lucky she's a beginner or she'd kick the crap out of me later . . .

'Please put my leg down,' she says. Embarrassed, I notice all the others are now padded up and sparring.

Please Put My Leg Down   *Roy Everitt*

'Would you put that down, please? And that. Yes, and that, too. They're not yours, they're mine and they are valuable. To me at least. Sentimentally and aesthetically. Quite vital to my emotional wellbeing, in fact. And yes, appearances *do* matter, especially in this business. Honestly, do you think it's easy, standing in this shop window all day, every day?'

Pool   *Perry Gretton*

She moved through the water with a dolphin's effortless grace, submerging and resurfacing with barely a ripple. Simon had been watching her for some time and now her head broke the surface directly below where he sat on a rocky ledge.

'Come and join me,' she said, extending her hand. He shook his head. She rose further from the water, her breasts glistening in the moonlight. 'Please . . .'

Floating on his back, he contemplated the twilit sky as she swam languidly around him. As his eyes began to close, she murmured, 'I have something to show you.'

She took his hand and led him far into the luminous depths until his lungs ached for relief. When he signalled to return to the surface, she clung to him with a fierce strength.

At dawn, the rising tide consumed the pool and the surrounding rocks, sweeping Simon's clothes far out to sea.

Pool   *Lynda Kenny*

The day they got the keys was the happiest of days. They ran up and down the stairs of the big old ramshackle house, opening windows, rubbing away grime to reveal oak floorboards, laughing at the sheer size of the overgrown garden. There was even a little ornamental pool. They couldn't believe their luck, that they could just afford the asking price. It was going to take a lot of work, but that only added to the excitement.

Two years later and the house was beautiful; painted white with black detailing. The gardens ablaze with colour and the pool gurgling in the sunlight. Drawn by the sound, the tow-haired toddler ran the length of the lawn on sturdy, chubby legs.

The day they left the house was the saddest of days.

Present   *Jill Paiton*

Mia's boyfriend, Adrian, had always lusted after a stronger kick from life; he discovered this in heroin. He was constantly in rehab.

Adrian handed Mia what was his first real sign of affection: a gold gift box. She frantically tore the box open; it revealed a carefully placed hypodermic and a small foil parcel.

'Happy twenty-first birthday, babe,' Adrian grinned.

Present   *Perry Gretton*

Silk ribbons laced with gold filigree tied the lilac box together.

'It's my daughter's birthday,' the middle-aged man told the driver as he got on the bus.

'How lovely,' she replied.

Fiddling with the ribbon, he sat right at the back where no-one would notice him. When he got off the bus, he left the present behind.

Queuetopia   *Richard Chalu*

'Yeah, and on Coruscant, where Obi-Wan's cloak gets caught on a ThreePO unit's transceiver?'

'Anakin's cloak, dude. Obi-Wan's cloak is Dantooine Bantha-Hair, only worn by Jedi Knights. It hangs differently. No way could it've—'

'Look! There's Ched. HEY, CHED!'

'Dude's an hour late, and his uniform's wrong. Those boots are for Stormtroopers, not Imperial Officers.'

'Dweeb.'

'Ched, you're late.'

'Sorry. Stopped at KFC. They're doing Pepsi cups with Yoda lids.'

'Cool.'

'What's the ETP?'

'ETP?'

'Estimated Time to Premiere.'

'I'll check. Six weeks, four days, ten hours, forty-two minutes and twelve seconds. Queue's building, dude. Three now. Wanna doughnut?'

'Sweet.'

Queuetopia   *Maxwell Mutami*

A real disease of nations that are in economic recession. Viral disease mainly caused by economic mismanagement. First symptom that causes severe headache is fuel shortage. Fuel shortage fuels other symptoms to compete for national, if not international, attention. Basic commodities begin having life-threatening high temperature of prices. Scarcity rears ugly face. Citizens are sparked by deadly panic and begin joining anything that looks like a queue. People queue for fuel, sugar, bread, cash at banks, transport and a host of other goods and services pertinent to survival. Recommended antiretroviral cure for this ailment: boot out reigning politicians.

Queuetopia   *Nathalie Boisard-Beudin*

High Hopes!

The song haunted him like a sweaty dream. But what weight

could Ant Lambda's dream have? None whatsoever. Condemned by alphabet rules to be in the same position in the ant alignment, he'd never make it to alpha rank. Or any other, for that matter. He was doomed to hold forever the same position, come wind or rain, war or harvest times.

In his dreams, he was on his own, roaming freely and unbound by arbitrary rules, away from lines dictated by tradition.

But which ant can ever be free?

Better step smartly.

High Hopes!

Quiet Room   *Carolyn Roberts*

Everyone had gone home. The children had left quickly, hugging their father as they went. None of them had offered to stay for the night. Loosening his black tie, Dougie sat down heavily in his chair. It faced across the room, towards a worn-out sofa that was sagging in the middle. But there was no-one sitting on it now.

Quiet Room   *Robert Capps*

The room was graveyard silent. The blue-eyed youth strode defiantly past the grey-haired old lady, her knitting needles halted, crucifix frozen. Onlookers seeing a scene from a shoot-'em-up Western, jangling spurs replaced by the fob chain from nostril connected to right ear. Within three strides, he was at his dad's bedside sobbing: 'I love you.'

Rage Against Time   *Indie Codanda*

The first wrinkle appeared at thirty-four. She was watching closely only for grey hair, so this wrinkle came as a dreadful shock. She felt so unprepared, unready. It marked a crossing and there was no going back. As her tears fell, she raged. Less attractive now, her fate seemed permanent. How could she reconcile the wrinkle with her virginity?

Rage Against Time   *Lynda Kenny*

In the pale, liquid light of the moon, the countess rose from her blood-red bath and studied her milk-white skin. Imagining an imperfection, she shrieked in rage and ran to the dungeon, baring her teeth. With one swift movement, the tainted blood was spilled onto the stone floor as the others, chained to the walls, screamed and pleaded.

Right Decision   *Gavin Parish*

The image on Mr Hutchinson's TV set was repeated nationwide, across all channels. Millions witnessed the grainy, almost spectral, figure making its appeal.

'This is a message from your future. You have an election pending and it is vital that you do not vote for Culwell. Vote for anyone but Culwell, I implore you. He will be the death of all mankind. We are the last survivors, dying of radiation sickness. Please heed our warning; it is your, and our, only hope.' As the image faded, Mr Hutchinson snorted loudly.

'If they think I'm voting Tory, they've another thing coming.'

Right Decision   *Tamzin Mole*

There was something terrible about the sight of blood on the pure white feathers of the swan. The image stained my eyes: vivid red on white, floating in a pool of green.

I did not stop to think. I stepped trembling into the December waters until green algae covered my waist. I was shaking, not with cold, but with fear, clinging with both fists to my trusty swan-hook. My wheelchair looked lonely on the bank.

The swan opened one eye and raised its head. Then, with a great flapping of wings, it sped off to the far side, out of reach.

Right Decision   *Teri Davis-Rouvelas*

It was true. Muffin looked out of it, her tail barely wagging, her once-shining eyes now dull with pain and fever.

'Tell me what you want,' he whispered. 'Do you think you can get better? I don't know if this is the right thing to do.'

Muffin stretched out in an attempt to lick his hand. He reached to scratch behind her ears.

'I guess we'll do what you said, Doc. I don't want to see her like this.'

After he left the vet's he sighed. Time to go to the hospice to visit his cancer-riddled mother.

Satin   *Kevin Connolly*

Satin and silk go together like . . . the first kiss and the first slap; something for the weekend and the morning-after pill; public bragging and itchy privates; a baby's first smile and the tiny pitter-patter of a noncommittal father's running boots.

Satin underwear is the only thing in the world that can make a silk purse out of a sow's rear.

Satin   *Anne Rainbow*

'Lot twenty: a fine watercolour entitled *Satin* by local artist Stephen Thomas. Who will start? Two hundred and fifty pounds?'

Lisa smiled at the thought of slipping between his sheets and winked at Stephen hiding in the wings of the auction hall.

'Lady in blue, thank you. Any more? No? Going, going, gone!'

As the gavel banged, Lisa realised what she was wearing . . .

Satin
Teri Davis-Rouvelas

He bought her the white satin gown for their fifth-anniversary celebration. He'd wanted to go dancing "like in the old days". They practised and anticipated what was sure to be a perfect evening.

And now he'd gone and ruined it – both the anniversary and the gown. Certainly, she was prettier than his dental hygienist.

Especially dressed in red satin.

Satin
Arthur Chappell

Satan sat in satin, learning Latin. Someone let the cat in.

'There's two hundred pages of this drivel, you say?'

'Yes, at least. Would you like to hear more?'

'No. It's diabolical.'

'You don't like it?'

'It's torture.'

'Can I recite my rhymes to the audience?'

'Of course. Keep repeating it throughout eternity . . .'

'Thanks, Dad.'

'Okay, Beelzebub . . .'

Second-Hand
Lee Henderson

'Hey, Mum. What's this, then? I thought you said it'd be a new one? It don't even 'ave any speakers; there ain't no scanner, nor a burner or even a cordless mouse. Cripes, Mum, if Dad woz alive, he would've bought a new one, not a second-hand one. Hey, Mum, what's wrong? Why yuh crying? Mum . . .'

Second-Hand   *Clarissa Henry*

She looked at her daughter and lost her temper: 'Reading again, second-hand books, second-hand lives, living vicariously.'

The girl looked up, then went on reading.

Years later, her mother proudly said, 'I always knew you could do it,' as she read the dedication on the flyleaf of her daughter's prize-winning novel:

For my mother, without whom . . .
With all my love.

Second Hand   *Darren Wheatley*

The slow, slow metronome beat of the second hand numbs, suffocates and smothers as moment after aching moment ticks lethargically away. The waiting is everything, piling upon itself, as if I'm outside of the normal flow of time itself.

Eventually, she returns.

'What do you think, the carmine or the cerise?'

Lips turn dry as I delay my inevitably incorrect answer.

Secret Formula   *Gavin Damerell*

What luck! he thought as he peered into the half-light, spotting the elusive Loch Ness Monster. *I'm rich!* he thought as he first focused his camera on the beast's famous curved spine, then next along its vast and powerful neck.

'You idiot!' he then moaned aloud when he realised his mistake and removed his not-so-impressive finger from the camera lens.

Secret Formula   *Anatoly Kudryavitsky*

The philosopher's stone is the boulder with which a Roman legionary crushed Archimedes's head. There're similar boulders set aside somewhere for each philosopher. We now know that the combination of the three components – a philosopher, a barbarian and a boulder – is the formula of the philosopher's stone, which was much sought-after by medieval alchemists, but remained beyond their comprehension.

(Translated from the Russian by the author.)

Secret Keys   *Estelle Kirk*

Donald's mind wrestled with the abstract beauties of the Space-Time Continuum as he did the washing up. He always helped old Mrs Seagrove after school.

Mrs Seagrove was searching her shelves for her secret keys for Donald to look after while she was in hospital. Opening an old painted tea tin, she pulled out a rusty key and pressed it into his hand.

He jiggled the key in the lock of the pantry door until at last it opened and an unexpected breeze blew back his hair. Inside, he saw the universe stretching away into the mists of the unknown.

Secret Keys   *Darren Wheatley*

You found the secret keys to my soul, you did. I led you straight to them. Bright and shiny, lying in your hand, my gift of exquisite trust. You turned them over, twisting through your quick fingers, a balancing act, played out on the sharp, serrated edge of your spite, hidden deep beneath the calm waters of your baleful blue eyes. And when you walked out, the keys to my softly slammed front door lay glinting on the coffee table, with a brief and bitter note. But you broke off the secret set in the lock. There were no duplicates.

Secret Passage   *Jill Paiton*

John had found it an arduous task seeing his parents. He kept asking himself how he could have put them through this ordeal. John was quite prepared to languish in the prison and did not want his parents involved. However, the Indonesian police wanted the publicity to deter others tempted to smuggle drugs. His name and identity were splashed all over the Australian news. John thought about his dad's cryptic comment when he handed him the jar of vegemite.

'Safe passage,' his dad had whispered to him.

John stared at the capsule taped inside the lid of the vegemite jar.

Secret Passage   *Estelle Kirk*

Emily's bedroom had a secret passage that led from dreary suburbia to a monastery in the mountains of Bhutan. She often returned with snow on her boots and sacred bread in her pockets.

Robert knew there was a secret passage from inside the dusty cupboard in the corner of the classroom. It led away from maths to a faraway island where he swam with speckled turtles.

Miss Brightstone had asked them all to write about a secret passage. Jane chewed her fingernails down to the quick. She couldn't follow her imagination; it had been punched out of her at home.

Secret Passage   *Sarah Star*

Dan had never had much to say. No-one thought to listen, so he stopped talking. Outside, down in the tunnels under London's rumbling streets, he picked up a dropped spray can and made his first mark. Words tumbled out that he wrote up in the dark, while the people, too wrapped up in themselves, hurried past, never looking to see the wisdom of the poems he wrote in secret. Maybe a few found them when they stopped to reflect why it was that they didn't talk to each other anymore. And when they did, Dan was finally heard.

Self-Deception   *Richard Chalu*

My foot overhung the ledge. The building was high; my worth low. The siren remained beyond reach, wanting me, the unwanted. She floated serenely in the air, ever looking at me in the way no-one living ever had. She loved me, the unloved.

Come, she whispered on the breeze.

I stepped forward.

Self-Deception   *Perry Gretton*

Though he thought otherwise, he was a lousy lover. A butcher's hands – one in a hurry to shut up shop at that – and the imagination of a rock lobster. As he groaned to his conclusion, I cried out in mock exultation.

'Was it good for you, darling?' he asked.

'The best.'

The fool believed me . . . but I was the bigger fool.

Shadow   *Gavin Damerell*

'Goodnight, sweetheart. God bless.' Katie suppressed a tear as she kissed her son on the forehead. *He need not know,* she thought. *Not yet, anyway.*

She turned off the bedside lamp that had cast her doubt over her son's sleeping form, and closed the bedroom door, thus leaving him still blissfully unaware of the cancerous shadow suffocating her from within.

Shadow *Mark Buchanan*

Soundless I stalk, shifting with your every breath. Crouching, stretching, I follow footstep to footstep. A dark side little noticed, I flit and slither around you, sometimes shrinking to disappear and hide beneath your shoes. But as night draws in, growing so much bolder, I stand tall. Then, when the lights go out, I'll fill your world and swallow you.

Shadow *Nicky Philips*

She shuffles slowly along the road, leaning heavily on her walking stick. Each step takes forever; each metre stretches to infinity. Cold penetrates tired bones; her worn-down joints ache constantly; pain furrows lines on a once-beautiful face. Shadows gather in the distance. Her time has come. Soon, she will escape the shackles of a failing body and soar free.

Shadow *Carolyn Roberts*

Leaving the office, Alan reviewed his day. He had signed off two new policies, given three interviews and spoken well in the House. So why didn't he feel satisfied? He sighed as he unlocked his car, knowing he would always be busy but never achieve real change. That was both the joy and the curse of being a Shadow Minister.

Shame *Roy Weltman*

My eyes open; I sit up. There are no curtains or blinds on my windows. I see the darkness outside, mixed with the skylight of the city. I will not be able to go back to sleep, for I am afraid of the feeling of paralysis overcoming me. The breeze is good, refreshing and calming. No more bad dreams for me tonight, just dark sleep.

I remember the first time I killed. The deal that was made after that: being recruited, and now a professional killer. I doze off, sitting on a chair with my feet on the coffee table.

Shame   *Nicky Philips*

Checking perfection in the mirror, Anne spotted Laura waiting for the limo to whisk them to her eighteenth celebration and a lump formed in her throat. Raising a child alone is difficult, especially for a supermodel, but the rewards had justified every gruelling second: such striking beauty, such joy.

But should she have swapped her hideous infant that first night?

Shell-Shocked   *Roy Weltman*

The dust clouds clear, revealing the aftermath of battle. I sit in a daze of body parts all over. I notice a bloody leg and I recognize the boot. My head battles the heat and my back carries the weight. I can only look down, for I have no more pride. Vultures soar; the arena will be cleared for tomorrow's battle.

Show Up   *Elizabeth Madden*

Spent all day getting ready: conditioning, moisturising, waxing and plucking – even had a go with the anti-cellulite ointment on my orange-peel thighs! Tried on everything in wardrobe – damn pre-menstrual bloating! Even "magic pants" useless in desperate case like mine!

Went shopping; perfect outfit! Understatedly sexy; *le chic Français*. Piled on the make-up; got there early.

The bastard!

Silent Passion   *Gavin Parish*

George moved into the apartment block about six months ago and started seeing Claire soon afterwards. The places he saw her were mostly on the stairs, in the lift, and getting into her little Volkswagen Beetle.

After a while, he started seeing her everywhere: the supermarket, jogging in the park, entering and leaving her place of work. Sometimes he saw her out with friends, or on a date. All this time, she remained unaware of his presence, though his passion grew and could only remain silent for so long.

Today, he was waiting in her flat when she arrived home.

Silent Passion   *Steven Schusman*

"It" was over; but it wasn't. In full flight, it had been too potent and too compelling, with too many innocents at risk if it took its inevitable course. And so they agreed to end it. The pain of not continuing had surely to be less than that of the alternative: recriminations and shattered childhoods.

The original pre-"it" contentedness of their lives was, however, gone; irretrievable, absorbed by the moment of the affair. Yet their lives were necessarily intertwined and would remain so. The passion remained, unextinguished, unexpressed and unbearably silent. She was his sister-in-law.

Silent Passion   *Hazel Buckingham*

Every Thursday evening, I saw her at the same spot – just beside the school's iron gates. She never appeared to notice me, always hiding her face behind her long brown hair. I was late leaving yesterday, so by the time I'd got to our regular passing place, she'd gone – or so I'd thought. I'd taken a couple of lazy paces – head down, thinking about her – before realising someone was beside me. She smiled nervously, mouthed something and then signed three little words.

'Fancy a drink?'

Being a teacher in the adult education deaf school does have its advantages.

Silent Passion
Sarah Star

Tenderly, she plucks the blood-red cherries from the trees, letting them lie like juicy hearts in the bowl, pure and luscious, their cold, hard stones removed. Sugar sprinkled lovingly on top is stirred in deep. Flames ignite to warm it through, and her spoon sinks into the ruby fruit, stirring in all her devotion.

Cooled, sealed and contained, it remains dormant until, unwrapping the covers, he discovers it, virgin and untouched. Immediately, he dips in his spoon and brings it to his lips. Oh, how delectable! He looks up and catches the shy smile of his wife gazing adoringly back.

Silent Passion
Darren Wheatley

She hasn't said a single word to me in six days. I have to hand it to her: the girl knows how to keep her word. Honestly, it was over nothing. I said something less than flattering about Brad and before I knew it, I'd rubbished every one of her "showbiz pals" from A-list to Z. It was cathartic – no way would I take it back. Like most girls, she knows how to stack the deck in her favour. She might've sworn not to make a sound to me until I apologised but she never said anything about touching . . .

Special
Sabrina Fatma Ahmad

He sits in a corner and doesn't speak to anyone. In a room full of self-proclaimed comedians, hip-hop freaks and footballers, he stands out, in his tattoos and painted nails and affinity for the dark, the deviant, and the different, because it resonates with how different he is. To them, he's an oddity; in my book, he's sheer magic.

Special
Rachiel Key

Red wine. Check! Steak with mashed potatoes. Check! Banana split. Check! Perfect. Everything is perfect. The table is all set. The music started serenading the room. Half past eight. Perfect. Last look in the mirror. Looking elegant in her blue-sequined dress, she posed a half-smile and a full smile. Act surprised! Are you sure you want to get married?

Special
Heidrun Knikander

In the never-ending darkness, there is snow and ice sparkling like diamonds. The sky draws colours more beautiful than a rainbow. Firs and pines are scattered over the friendless landscape. In their solitude, these crippled trees are fighting against the icy storms that are riding over the tundra. This lonely place is abandoned by humans and preserved for nature.

Stepping Stone
Teri Davis-Rouvelas

Each year, I've noticed the stepping stones get smaller. He replaces them, rearranges the path through the garden. The plants stay the same. Even the dead willow is still there, poison ivy clawing its way skyward, replacing the willow with shiny leaves from which the birds shy.

I want to tear the whole thing up, start over again. This was *her* garden, after all, and she left. He came to me, married me; she should be gone by now.

Gone like the birdsong. Gone like the stones and path soon, and then nothing will lead to the garden shed in the back. It'll rot, fall into the concave hole locked inside. Maybe this is what he wants. Maybe he knows. Maybe he smelled what wafted through the garden that first summer.

Maybe he's got the right idea. Except for her, I never used stepping stones. They can lead places.

Steps

Nina Simon

Footsteps draw closer. My eyes seek an escape, knowing there is none. I am too weak. Already, I can feel death's breath on my face.

The room's temperature drops. A dark shadow stands over my bed, sliding on top of me. Skeletal fingers fondle my breasts, circle my belly button. Every muscle tenses. I cannot fight him.

His hand plunges into my body, like a knife slipping through water. I scream. Nails hammer into my heart; fire burns through my body as I feel the last drops of life drain from my soul.

He departs, leaving behind an empty shell.

Sticky Fingers

Jenni Doherty

It's her mouth – pouting, but not coral pink – that Tony sees first. He feels spied on, sort of shelled. A fleeting, darting feeling ripples through him as he blushes on a stumble of words.

'Fish need feeding.' Schlooooop!

So many sucking Os blink on the humming surface, setting water bubbling. Tiny, all-seeing things gobble the fleshy pads of his fingertips, and from there to his guts something shoots. Gorgeous electricity, deep and delicious. Julie lifts her eyes. Dark blue-green to his pale blue-grey. Bluey-greeny-greyish-blue. And next to the gurgling aquarium, with sticky fingers, he turns and kisses her; floating.

Sticky Fingers *Christopher Spalding*

'I nearly made a mistake about who had taken the cake,' said Mrs Parker. The children obediently stopped what they were doing and turned to face her. 'In fact, I'd like to thank the little boy who just saved me making that mistake and for letting me know who the culprit really was.'

Thirty bony backsides shifted uneasily in their seats.

'So thank you, Thomas, for solving the mystery. As soon as you came to tell me it was Jack, I knew it must have been you, because when I shook your hand, it was you who had sticky fingers.'

Sticky Fingers *Mark Buchanan*

A line of bright dots streak across a sea of midnight and starlight, the slingshot solar sail ships speed away from a dying sun.

Huge fernlike hands slowly unfurl, forming vast shallow silver shuttlecocks that swallow the star fields ahead. Each hand has a million fingers and each finger a million mirrored sails shimmering in the solar breeze.

Navigating galactic tides and currents, they sleep while their interstellar sycamore seeds sail across oceans of oblivion. Outshining the sun with giant hands and sticky fingers, celestial somnambulists reach out to grasp eternity and wrest it from the grip of the gods.

Stillbirth *Steven Schusman*

'You're going to have a sister.'

Nine months, two weeks arrive. Expectant mother is dropped at the maternity unit; expectant father parks and rushes to the ward.

First the ultrasound, then the stethoscope and even the

ear trumpet. Doctor looks panicked and utters the diabolical words, 'I can't find the heartbeat.'

Several hours later, after choked calls to bewildered parents, labour concludes. In complete, crushing silence, a lifeless, otherwise perfect, child is delivered.

The registrar's customary greeting smile evaporates in embarrassment.

'Mummy, where's my sister?'

Empty pink bedroom. Every newborn a constant harsh reminder. A gravestone with a single date.

Stillbirth
Colin Biggs

'Are you happy now?' she chided.

Momentarily, I considered ignoring her. 'Happy? Yes, this child means that the work can progress. Each soul brings us closer to the time.'

'I know that, but this was no accident. You . . . you made this happen, placed your hands on the mother, told her everything would be fine.'

Removing my surgical mask, I slowly faced her. 'Look carefully, Sister Justine, consider what I am.'

She saw. Her scream became silenced, suspended forever in her slender throat. Washing the last of the blood from my hands, I prepared to meet the grieving "parents".

Still Life
Kitty Redding

I am bathed in afternoon sunlight. Monday, quiet, still, nothing to do. My gnarled fingers struggle with the cardigan buttons.

'Leave it on, Mavis, love. You'll catch cold.'

Hands now folded, a good girl, they say. The air is stale, heavy with death; I struggle to breathe.

In, out, in, out.

Cynthia is shouting. Ethel asks for her mother.

I gaze out the window and drift away – memories of Donald, long gone, laughing on the beach.

I smile. We made love in the sand dunes. My cheeks burn. In, out.

'She's going.'

No, there's still life in me yet.

Still Life   *Neil Outram*

It's difficult to discern how long I've been here – with your eyes shut, time becomes fluid, formless – I just know it feels like an eternity. An eternity of being trapped, a prisoner in my own body. They took my food tube out a few days ago. I wanted to scream, 'Don't kill me, I'm still alive!' but I don't know that I am anymore. This isn't even death; it's far worse. I can listen to life going on around me, but that's all. All I am is thoughts and feelings; frustration, anxiety, memories, depression, pain. Is this still life?

Still Life   *Liz Gallagher*

In the photo, I am in green Crimplene. I wear a red cap and slant to the left. My knee bends outwards towards the row of men standing together after church. They avoid eye contact and talk of passing away: there is a funeral or a wake on me. My brother is in his First Communion suit. He looks broad-shouldered. My mother is half-there. She is sliced down the middle with her leftness visible. Whoever did this had a shaky hand or a gripe. She is staring. Her hair is done-up. She looks tall. There is no sign of hardship.

Sub-Normal   *Colin Biggs*

As they brought the new group into the enclosure, I fought to remember my training and to suppress my involuntary arousal. Their labels – orange, deep, radiant orange – made them different, somehow lower. And yet behind the layers of filth, they appeared remarkably like us. We began. Unbelievably, one glared, almost aggressively, defying the club for as long as she could. Not long. Sweating and breathless, we confirmed each one. The leader gave the sign and, elated, we stood tall as the music played. I felt the pride triumph over the pity, and embraced the need to make our people strong.

Sub-Normal   *Gavin Parish*

'You may be wondering what brought me here today after all these years.'

One of the goons knocked Bob to the ground and put a boot in his stomach to keep him there. Another pointed a gun at his head. The boss man, reclining on Bob's sofa, considered his surroundings disdainfully.

'You mocked me, called me sub-normal. And that hurt.'

'But we were at school then . . .' Bob trembled.

'Now I've come up in the world and I've a lot of old scores to settle.'

'You can't do this!' Bob shook with fear.

'Kill him.'

'Yes, sir, Mister President.'

Surrender   *Clarissa Henry*

Tears rolled silently down the girl's cheeks. She sat hunched-up in the chair and spoke haltingly of her pain, her inability to go on living. Dr S listened, encouraging her, occasionally making notes on his pad. She saw him suppress a yawn. At the end of

141

the hour, he said, 'Same time next week.'

That night she committed suicide.

Tambourine   *Darren Wheatley*

Wide-awake, I feel so numb. The sleeping city sprawls before
me. Ancient empty streets lie dead and dreamless as a cold steel
dawn rises over the waiting rooftops. Restless, exhausted and
alone, I hear a jingle jangle: some old busker casting one last
mystical spell. I stare at my wandering boots and sigh. Right
now, I'd follow him anywhere.

Tambourine   *Carolyn Roberts*

Katy listened as the music conducted by Mr Sanders gained
momentum. She should have been at the front, leading the
choir. She hated him for placing her back here "to give someone else a chance" – meaning Emma, the new girl who had
become his favourite. Angrily, she shook her tambourine hard,
trying to drown out Emma's clear, pure voice.

Tarnished   *Elizabeth Madden*

He spends his days and nights in shop doorways, cap at his
feet, old dog under a blanket by his side. He drinks Red Biddy
and mutters threats at passers-by, who look on him with pity
or disdain.

The medals he earned for his courage are kept in his pocket,
blackened and tarnished by age and neglect.

Tarnished   *Shirley Bunyan*

The castle stood strong against the Scottish sky, almost to
attention, as the first glow of morning silhouetted its proud

stance. It had been the perfect venue for a perfect wedding. As I drew nearer, it seemed to show itself in a new light; grey, cold, foreboding. I wondered if it knew all along I would be returning here alone.

Tarnished
Carolyn Roberts

The family had arranged to meet at Gran's house after the funeral. Arriving early, Sandra walked slowly up the path, thinking about Gran's stubborn independence and the pride she used to take in her home. Once, a brass handle had gleamed triumphantly from the door, announcing that this was a respectable household. But now it hung heavily, unloved and tarnished.

Tempted
Karen Jones

After ten years of fidelity, she was about to kiss another man. It wasn't adultery; it was just a kiss.

She felt her heart quicken, her eyes close, her lips part. She felt his hands rest on her hips, his breath warm her cheek, his lips move closer.

Deep down, she knew: there's no such thing as "just a kiss".

Tempted
Richard Chalu

I keep telling myself this isn't real, that I am not me, but there she is, naked and smooth on my bed. She's smiling at me and I know it's time. Separated from my mates, my laddish bravado and cocky self-assuredness vanish. I swallow nervously. I know this moment is unique: my watershed. The hour I become a man.

The Ascent
Neil Outram

'Now I must join my father in heaven,' said Jesus, 'ably assisted by my lovely assistant, Anne!'

The crowd gasped as Jesus, dressed in nothing but a white shroud, was surrounded by a curtain of red silk held by the delectable Anne. Drum rolls ensued as the sheet billowed and shook. Then it dropped, revealing two discarded brown sandals. The watching minions gasped and applauded the fantastic spectacle.

'Up here!' hollered Jesus, flying high above them. 'Look, no strings!' he declared, waving his hands around his body.

The captivated crowd roared with appreciation, already anticipating the second coming: David Copperfield.

The Cheque
Darren Wheatley

The picture frame lay smashed, the door open, as he'd scurried feverishly to the bank. He'd been so proud when that first royalty cheque had slid from the envelope, the first of many. Or so he'd thought at the time.

Later, he smiled serenely at reflections from the broken shards while "one last fix" invaded and defeated his tortured system.

The Cure
Eileen Burzynska

How much longer does this go on? Waking up in the morning – yet again forcing food down, verbalising and interacting with other hostages to life, moving from one place to another, carrying out mundane tasks, breathing . . . Give me a break!

It slides darkly through the door and hovers, faceless with glinting sickle.

'I'm a little early but I have come.'

The Cure *Kevin Connolly*

'My wife's on her deathbed, but I've discovered a cure for all diseases.'

'Won't that result in everybody living forever, Vicar?'

'Yes. Including my wife.'

'People will lose all faith in the afterlife.'

'I don't care, Bishop. My wife's more important.'

'It'll lead to overcrowding. They'll ban sex.'

'Oops! I've spilled it! Oh, well, it probably wouldn't have worked anyway.'

The Dance *Karen Jones*

He brushed against her on the stairs, just a little too close. He held her gaze, knowing she'd be first to lower her eyes. He leaned forward, letting his breath stroke her neck as he whispered, 'Sorry.'

He felt the heat from her blush sear through his body, fuelling his fantasies. He'd taken the lead – the next move was hers.

The Dance *Julie Okon*

'Where is it?'

'Down in Ken Hall's barn.'

'Come on, let's go.'

Strobe-lit hay bales and twenty-odd bikers. Transformed from the milking and mucking out, all hair and black leather now in an emptied-out cow shed. First taste of shandy and dark dirty dancing. Status Quo and *Down, Down, Deeper and Down* blasting my veins.

The Debt Collector *Estelle Kirk*

She sat outside the coffee shop in the sunshine, watching the world go by. She wistfully noticed the belly-button rings, the flat bare stomachs, the skimpy floating fashions, and had another bite of her doughnut.

The debt collector had come for her youth and beauty, leaving her fat, wrinkled and grey. But he'd left behind her twinkly eyes, her laughter and her experience. She had a choice: being bitter and regretting the loss of youth or loving every moment of life that she had left. She still had dreams, one of which was to write her story.

The Debt Collector   *Darren Wheatley*

Ever since Charters won the Nobel Prize, he'd been uneasy. Perpetual motion had long been a scientific goal and Charters's solution, though brilliant, had been regarded with suspicion. Justly so.

Charters's device worked using an effect he called *Quantum Borrow*, but he'd allowed everyone to think otherwise. Maybe the ten-million-dollar prize had something to do with it. The worst of it was, he wasn't sure where the quanta he'd "borrowed" actually came from.

The doorbell rang. Answering it, Charters came face to chest with a tall, hooded figure.

'I believe you have something of ours,' it intoned darkly.

The Debt Collector   *Lynda Kenny*

Sarah had answered the ad on a whim. Momentarily heartbroken after a tiff with her boyfriend, the intriguing caption had caught her eye: *Been fired from your job? Been dumped by your partner? Let us help you redress the balance. All calls in confidence.*

She had forgotten about it. Mark called two days later and things were wonderful. So the neat package and covering letter came as a surprise. She opened and scanned the letter quickly;

and then again – slowly. The letter fell from her hand as she stared at the discreet logo on the package: *Pound of Flesh Collection Agency*.

The Edge of Christmas

Mark Buchanan

On the periphery, there's a precipice where darkness dwells, pendant and intangible; the summation of every place hidden from mind and memory. This is where the forgotten endlessly fall like so many silver-sixpenny well wishes; swallowed by oblivion – not even the screams can escape.

Slowly turning away from the edge, Nicholas dusts off his hands, chuckling, 'Ho, ho, ho!'

The Edge of Christmas

Gavin Damerell

Maud was sulking: she hated Christmas. She hated the music, children and the stupid frock she was forced to wear. But what she hated most of all were the pine needles up her backside.

What's the use of being a fairy if you can't fly away? she thought.

Maud sulked some more then kicked a bauble off the Christmas tree.

The End

Karen Jones

In the creeping darkness, I see the outlines of the balloons I hung this morning. In the blackness that has commandeered my soul, I hear your voice, feel the wounds your words inflicted. For years, you swore your love, your passion, your fidelity. Now it ends with you leaving on your birthday. What gift will *she* give you?

147

The End   *Lynda Kenny*

He sat forward in the shadows, watching. The fear in her eyes exceeded his expectations and sent a thrill to the core of him. He knew he was crossing over to a very dark place, but it only excited him more.

'Her punishment,' he whispered.

She screamed as they sliced. The end was swift but *so* satisfying.

He slumped back, spent.

The End   *Amy Rafferty*

Her mouth is sewn shut. Every cell in her body is silent, though her hair and nails still grow. Her pale skin recedes and turns black. Stomach and lungs, filled with gas, distend and push up through the dark, splitting the skin. She can hear her joy hum and throb as she feeds the earth that once fed her.

The End   *Clarissa Henry*

The music student climbed up to the gods. Standing room only. He looked down and saw a pinpoint in the orchestra pit. The conductor lifted his baton. The grand old man put down his baton and turned to acknowledge the standing ovation. He looked up and saw the young student whose dream had been to stand where he stood today.

The Envelope   *Teresa Stenson*

When they find the envelope, they'll understand.

Remember when we met that night? That night of the dance, and we danced, danced, danced . . . to whatever they played. We didn't care.

Once you said, 'What will we do when the other dies?' I

pressed my cheek to yours and hoped I'd go first. You choose the music for our final dance.

On the bed, you reach for my hand. I hurt, I ache, I look at you . . . I think, *thank you, my love*. But you say it first. We go quietly with the music.

When they find the envelope, they'll understand.

The Envelope   *Perry Gretton*

The letter arrived on Monday, hand-addressed to David. His wife placed it on his study desk.

On Wednesday, she noticed it remained unopened. When she mentioned it to him at dinner, he said, 'Don't worry, I'll get around to it eventually.'

By Friday, overwhelmed by curiosity, she took the letter into the kitchen, steamed it open, and read the contents. In David's handwriting, it said, *You just had to open it, didn't you?*

The bastard! She sealed the envelope and flattened it with a warm iron before replacing it exactly where she'd found it. Now she would test his patience.

The Envelope   *Sam Robinson*

For sixty years, I've treasured a copy of *Mrs Beeton's Household Management* for the envelope inside it addressed to Miss (the first "s" written long, like an "f") Agnes Thwaites.

'Dearest Aggie,' the letter dated 8 October 1835 inside the envelope reads, 'I love you. Would you do me the honour of becoming my wife? Yours affectionately, Frank.'

My great-grandmother gave the book to my mother, who gave it to me. Now *Mrs Beeton* sits on my kitchen shelf, enveloping the enveloped letter in her womb, mocking my life. If I'd been loved, I might have had a daughter, too.

The Envelope *Karen Jones*

When Cerys awoke, she saw the white lie resting on the pillow. It seemed to throw the light at her eyes, stinging them. But the silence hurt the most.

He had gone and, like the others, he hadn't bothered with "goodbye". What was it about Cerys that demanded the stealth exit and an envelope placed deftly on a dented pillow? She put it in her bedside cabinet with the others, next to her new gun. She had warned him – no bailing without a civil conversation. He hadn't listened.

She'd make him listen, make him explain, and make him gone forever.

The Ferryman *Arthur Chappell*

'Relax. You won't drown. You're already dead.'

'It's like swimming in quicksand.'

'Just tread blood. It's thicker than water.'

'Were you thrown overboard, too?'

'Yes, and for the same reason as everyone else. I asked Charon how he got a girl's name.'

'Will he rescue us?'

'Not for an eternity. We're all in a bit of a Styx . . .'

The Ferryman *Lee Henderson*

He had that furtive, fidgety look of someone about to embarrass both himself and his companions. Earlier, I had succumbed to karaoke madness, singing *Avalon* in an embarrassing imitation of Bryan Ferry *sans* Roxy Music. Now I felt only *Schadenfreude* as I realised there was more than one Ferryman in the club.

Let's Stick Together, he warbled. Sheer joy!

The First Time *Kevin Connolly*

I'll never forget the first time I didn't make love. Four solid hours we didn't spend getting hot and sweaty. Just thinking about all the fumbling and thrashing about we didn't get up to still brings water to my eyes. She wasn't my first love, but she was easily the most beautiful woman I never got to wake up with.

The First Time *Eileen Burzynska*

'You were absolutely right. This fruit's delicious,' said Adam rapturously. Eve smiled seductively and the serpent slithered away devilishly. 'And now we know as much as God.'

As he spoke, his happiness started to drain away as he saw stretching ahead, years of sadness, drudgery and pain.

Eve looked at herself for the first time: 'God, I've put on weight!'

The First Time *Mark Burns*

Pete swallowed and rubbed his sweaty palms on his trouser legs as she nestled in beside him, her chunky thigh grazing his. She took his hand in hers.

'Strong, flexible fingers. Ideal,' she purred with calm authority. After all, she was much older and highly experienced.

'You'll enjoy this, I promise. Playing piano is pure pleasure.'

The Gift *Lee Henderson*

A roughly wrapped package placed on a doorstep; eye watching. Young man hides behind a parked car and throws a stone at the door. A single shot echoes out, impacting, spinning him about, blood spraying. Door opens, a young woman screams, runs to him, cradles his head.

A fiancée's birthday gift, a Coalition soldier's nightmare. Both sides destroyed.

The Gift   *Stephen Reilly*

Rain pelted against the windscreen. He glanced in the rear-view mirror and saw his son's Down's syndrome features and sightless eyes. Familiar anger flashed within him at a god, who, if he existed, didn't care.

The boy screamed. Involuntarily, he leaned hard on the brakes.

A heartbeat later, a tree smashed into the road, its outer branches nestling against the bonnet.

The Gift   *Eileen Burzynska*

He pressed his body sensuously against her as he passed through the kitchen, grunting in happy anticipation of the dinner she was lovingly preparing: chopping, filleting, seasoning. She returned the pressure, tweaked his ear and dabbed him on the nose with a floury finger. The back door was slightly ajar, revealing his offering to her: a flattened, slightly desiccated mouse.

The Gift   *Clarissa Henry*

The middle-aged man was in intensive care. Time was running out. Eight hundred miles away, a young man was driving at top speed. His car skidded and overturned. He was pronounced dead on arrival at the hospital. The surgeons worked quickly. The life-saving container was sent, and two hours later the transplant began. A second-hand heart – the gift of life.

The Gift
Perry Gretton

He clasps the blood-red rose into my hands. 'You are yet love-lier even than this magnificent bloom.'

Tears bedim my eyes as he tenderly kisses my cheek, whispering, 'Pray, keep thyself safe until my return.'

As I watch him ride away, the rose drops to the ground. Pressing thorn-pricked hands to my lips, I suck the blood from my wounds.

The Graveyard Shift
Arthur Chappell

'Oh Jesus!'

'John Smith's a quite common name. I stole my own grave-stone. Look.'

'He died in eighteen twenty-three.'

'Well, when I die, chisel in my date of birth and death. Do you know what tombstones cost these days?'

'I knew you were cheap, but . . .'

'So you won't go back tonight and help me pick out a coffin?'

The Graveyard Shift
Jill Paiton

'It was tedium that sounded the death knell for him, you know. If you ask me, he was fed up with everything and everyone in his life toward the end: too many parasites wanting their pound of flesh. There's never a dull moment working security at his graveside, though. Better hang up now, Mum. The Elvis Memories Tour is starting.'

The Homecoming
Darren Wheatley

Staring across the rundown playing fields where he'd scored his first goal, kissed his first girl, smoked his first cigarette and made his first deal, he hesitated as a single salty tear coursed

153

down his cheek. After all this time, the emotion of the occasion never failed to bite as he was swept once again to that first time, over twenty years ago. The shrill of a car phone broke his reverie and he turned his back on the scene to take the call, but not until he witnessed the powerful steel maw of the giant earthmover make its first incision.

The Homecoming   *Dan Purdue*

Albert loosened his black silk tie. He removed his shoes and cufflinks. He stood by the window, watching bumblebees. The grandfather clock dispensed long, lonely chunks of time.

He turned around. Mary's armchair wasn't just empty; it was a hole in the world where a person belonged. Her gardening magazine wilted over one arm; knitting yarns peeked from a paper bag beside her slippers.

Albert felt a plunging sadness and went into the kitchen. As the kettle whistled, he broke down. By the teapot stood a tragedy in miniature, placed there by uncounted years of routine: two teacups, waiting, side-by-side.

The Homecoming   *Jenni Doherty*

Something calls you home: that scent of dusk; a whispered doorway charm; the brush of midnight blues on jazz of cities true where tempt of corner streets let secrets spill in heat; where haunts of other towns and beggars, buskers, clowns remind you once of Wilde and youth and where you used to be.

A nostalgic nudge: smudged memories of what could have been, should have been. Yes, I was bold then. Bowled over then. It was the music, the mood, the company, the world; word on word making sense, making sentences, making out, making love . . . breaking free. That's home.

The Homecoming
Maxwell Mutami

After years of forced exile, Maki returned home. High expectations of improved life were what he cherished. Local newspapers had always painted a heavenly picture of the new-born African state. Talk was of booming industries and massive housing projects.

As the cab groaned and puffed, arguing its way through gullied streets of his childhood location, Maki could not believe his eyes and nose. A Mississippi of raw sewage flooded the sandy, potholed streets. Odd smells suffocated the air. Crowded wooden shacks characterised the entire neighbourhood.

'Not ten years after guns were put into mute-mode,' grumbled Maki, head shaking disapprovingly.

The Invention
Steven Schusman

His boys were the apples of his eye. He'd be there on dank Sunday mornings, cheering and exhorting from the touchline. His sons' friends were all envious of the coolest dad in the class.

He could convert a try from forty yards and down a yard of ale in the time most men would need to sink a pint; for his party piece, he'd extinguish the dying barbeque embers from fifteen feet.

He reeled off the dirtiest jokes with aplomb. His wolf whistle was without compare, and his unnoticed stolen glances were all confined to the men's changing room.

The Invention
Neil Outram

'You're so stunning. I love you,' whispered Roger, stroking the face of his sleeping Erotobot – new for 2080, with ultra-realistic breasts and bottom.

Six months ago, he bought her. The blonde model was sold out, so he opted for the brunette: five feet-six inches, 34C-22-32.

Her name was Anna, and with her state-of-the-art software, she could love, lust and even form opinions. She seemed more human than the real women Roger dated before he ventured into Robance.

After a quiet whirring noise from her activating hardware, Anna opened her eyes, engaged her empathy chip, then released a tear.

'Roger, I've met someone.'

The Interval   *Estelle Kirk*

Yards of dusty, blood-red velvet fell gracefully to the stage. Diamonds sparkled amongst the restless audience, while backstage, noiseless bustle prepared the tawdry scenery for the final act.

Desdemona sat, breathless and joyous, anticipating a scripted embrace that might hold real passion. Othello waited in the wings, looking beyond the footlights. He could see the touch of fingers, the glance of love between the two men in the front row. His heart was breaking.

The curtain lifted to find him in throes of passion, about to kill his Desdemona. But the tears that coursed down his black greasepaint were real.

The Interval   *Gavin Parish*

An empty house. Certain things I soon miss, now that I'm on my own. It's all my fault, of course. All those years of taking her for granted. A reckless indiscretion that made me realise, too late, how much she meant to me.

'I'm sorry,' I tell her on the phone tonight, knowing my words sound hollow, meaningless.

At the other end, a muted sob she'd rather I didn't hear. 'I need more time.' The line goes dead. Please, let her be more forgiving than I would be. This might be the end, but I'm praying it's just the interval.

The Interval
Karen Jones

As the cast returned to their dressing rooms, Alison checked the props for the last act. She walked along the blue-lit corridors, careful to keep her footsteps soft, maintaining the silent magic of the backstage world. She found the prop dagger for the death scene lying on the table in the prompt-side dock and quickly replaced it with the one secreted in the pocket of her blacks. If she couldn't have him, no wide-eyed RADA graduate would.

'Ladies and gentlemen, this is your beginners' call for Act Three,' her soft voice seeped seductively through the intercom. 'Final positions, please.'

The Learner
Darren Wheatley

There are some lessons you never forget, some lessons you should never have to learn, and there are some that you know you have to pass on, no matter what. Ellie was my first; she taught me how to love and she taught me how to hate.

Once again, I wish I knew how to pass on the right lesson.

The Learner
Kevin Connolly

'It's fine,' the doctor said. 'We're all afraid of it because it's a novel experience. But you'll be surprised by the result.'

'You'll love it,' the Vicar said. 'You'll have a fantastic time.'

'Okay,' I finally agreed, closing my eyes.

'Hello!' a booming voice! 'New here, aren't you? Don't worry. You're only a learner, but heaven is a lovely place.'

The Light
Perry Gretton

By the flickering candlelight, I pen my journal. I have much to record after an eventful day hunting for food. To relieve the aching cold, I breathe on my mittened hands and continue writing until I can no longer hold the quill.

Outside, the wind howls and the snow creeps further up the window. I go over to where three of my huskies huddle in front of the meagre fire and lie with them to draw some warmth into my body. Unwittingly, I fall asleep.

When I awake, the fire is almost out. I throw on some sticks, and when they do not catch light, stab at the embers and blow on them. They do not respond. *Damnation!*

The only paper I have is my journal. I am out of matches, but at least I still have the candle. As I retrieve the notes, the candle gutters and dies.

The Light   *Darren Wheatley*

You hadda be there to understand. It was a club, an old and respected brotherhood. We watched each other's backs, took care of families when one of the guys went away. If you weren't in, you were out; and if you were out, you were a nobody.

I was somebody. Old guys on the street paid respects; kids queued up to clean my car or even my shoes. Back then, it meant something. We took the American Dream by the lapels and shook it for all it was worth. And then shook it some more just for fun. We thought it would last forever.

Nothing lasts forever. I know that now. Maybe we got too greedy; maybe we forgot there was anything wrong with what we were doing. That's all behind me now. It came to me on my Last Night:

In nomine Patris et Filii et Spiritus Sancti . . .

The Light   *Karen Jones*

The customer lifted a tiny, pearlescent jar.

'Excellent choice, madam. The fjord range; glides across skin with glacial grace. Only seven hundred and forty-nine pounds,' Clarice said.

158

The woman tapped a box. 'And this?'

'Egyptian, scented mud; one thousand, seven hundred and ninety-nine pounds.'

The customer spotted the glowing jar.

'What's that?'

Clarice grabbed it. 'I'm sorry, that one is reserved.'

'Reserved? Do you know who I am?'

'There's a waiting list,' Clarice whispered. 'It's distilled luminosity. All the rage with our VIP clients – but very rare.'

'I want it.'

'Well, I really shouldn't . . . but since it's my last day . . .'

'How much?'

'Three thousand, five hundred pounds.'

'I'll take it.'

'I'll wrap it.'

Clarice turned away, removed the cycle light from the jar and wrapped the empty purchase with calico and ribbon.

'Keep the lid sealed. Use the "waft" attachment,' she cautioned. 'It'll last longer. If you're not happy, just return it. My replacement will be delighted to help.'

The Long Journey   *Tamzin Mole*

They pulled each other up the sheer rock. On the shore below, the upturned lifeboat sheltered those too weak to climb. On another frozen shore, seven hundred miles across open ocean, the shipwrecked crew awaited their return. Only the black cliff separated them from civilisation and salvation.

Nearly at the summit, their leader urged them onwards. 'The worst is behind us now, lads. One last push . . .'

Driven by hunger, exhausted beyond endurance, they reached the ridge and silently looked over. A vast landscape of frozen mountains stretched ahead as far as the eye could see.

'Bugger,' said Shackleton.

The Long Journey   *Gary McMahon*

Standing room only. Looming, leather-clad, piston-driven hips lunge at him at every kink in the track. She swings his peripheral vision round her ripplesome pelvis like an astral hula-hoop. Stretch-leather creaking, rolling rhythm, back arching in a tunnel bend, glossblackglossblack. Her crotch lurches and snatches back to save his face in the nick of time. Arms handrail high, gloss-tight balloons pop his ears. Dusky musk floods his senses until blackglossblackgloss imprints on his memory for the rest of his life. Her lustrous gaze browbeats the lad until he stands ᵘᵖ for her. The journey was seven and three-quarter inches long.

The Long Journey   *Azfarul Islam*

I couldn't believe it: she was married now. I'd grown up with my cousin, so her presence was taken for granted. Would all the arguments, the fights, the grudging apologies and shared secrets be an evanescing memory? How about the times I feigned ignorance to her parents of the furtive dates and daring escapades she had with her betrothed? Turbid times, those . . . but memorable nonetheless. The house would certainly be many times quieter and certainly less enjoyable . . .

But I promised myself: no long goodbyes. Her hubby was the neighbour's son, so she was just moving in next door.

The Long Journey   *Heidrun Knikander*

I drive through the darkness of the night; here and there are some lights. People are watching TV; I envy them for their peace. I lived in many different places, foreign countries, but I never felt like being at home. All those years I was alone, although surrounded by many people; friends that are not friends. Out in the darkness of the woods, there is only nature and me. I know every single tree in this forest. A deer at the roadside says hello. Even the owl that starts flying seems to greet me. I am on my way home.

The Long Journey   *Darren Anderson*

Twenty thousand years ago, a glacier pitched, heaving down the mountainside, streeling bedrock into the glen where it lay and waned away in the days and nights. Until today raised by a drift of urchins, who bounce them zinging off the perspex windows and wake-startle the nodding sleepers.

Two thousand years ago, an affiliate of the Red Branch, bandling on horseback through brushland, had his scalp prised open at speed by a pack of mead-sodden braggarts.

One thousand years ago, a soothsayer foresaw that in the distant future, a metal dragon would haunt the seafront, storming back and forth somewhere on this causeway.

The Long Journey   *Sabrina Fatma Ahmad*

He stood under the street lamp, bright against the darkening evening. A cigarette hung limply from his lips, unlit. My best friend – a complete stranger.

I remembered the first day we met. He'd been standing with his back to the window, a dark silhouette against the glare of the noontime sun, rolling a cigarette. A rebel.

One year between then and now. Twelve months of mutual discovery, deepening into friendship before withering as his restless spirit grated against my need to be grounded.

Now he stood, poised for flight as we said our goodbyes. As if our journey together never happened.

The Mask
Shirley Bunyan

Stella's friend regarded her incredulously.

'What! You turned him down?'

'Yes, I turned him down.'

'But it's the chance of a lifetime.'

'I can't risk it, Kim. Not again. Anyway, there's my career. I'm not about to up and leave for Australia at the drop of a hat. Not for anybody.'

'But he isn't just anybody, is he?'

Stella took a deep breath, 'No, he isn't just anybody.'

He was the stars, the moon, the universe. Much too much to lose. She had no choice but to throw it away.

Once alone, Stella took off the mask and wept.

The Mask
Lynda Kenny

Shackled in her own dungeon, the countess strained and fought against the bloodstained chains. She rained down curses on the heads of the villagers who had silently, and with eyes averted, started to build the little wall. Haughty still, she spoke of the terrors that awaited any peasant who had dared to touch her.

When the wall had reached chest height, she sobbed pitifully and pleaded for her life, promising pardons for all and riches for the one who set her free.

When the brick mask reached her terror-filled eyes, she began to scream. The screams could be heard for eleven days.

The Mask
Mark Buchanan

The hissing black mask descended towards my face, smothering me with the smell of rubber and talc.

'Now, count backwards from ten, taking deep breaths, please,' said a voice.

The bright light above me shrank to a pinpoint as I slid

down a deep, dark funnel, pursued by a swarm of bees.

My head felt strangely unfamiliar when I woke later, and my body seemed baggy. As my eyes struggled to focus, I noticed my arms looked grey and aged. It was only when I saw the next bed that it became clear: I had donated far more than a kidney.

The Meaning of Life   *Gavin Damerell*

In the past, during his lectures, he often stated to his students that it was perhaps the one and only question that could never be truly answered.

Now, however, he is preparing to change his notes. For when he tells the very same students that yesterday, he held his beautiful newborn baby – and now the answer – in his loving arms.

The Meaning of Life   *Indie Codanda*

His principles of kindness and goodness defined a life of uneventful existence. Always a cog in the wheel, he was never an influencer of many. Now on his deathbed, he pondered this essence of goodness. Is an unblemished life of no consequence better than a questionable life of impact?

His biggest regret in dying was the lack of resolution.

The Mistress   *Hazel Buckingham*

From an early age, I knew she'd be My Mistress. Stella was her name and she was a cool Belgian blonde. I remember the first time I held her beautiful, smooth form in my hand. She felt so right, so good and she made me feel complete. With her intoxicating love, I could do anything; I was brave, fearless and invincible. My mates knew her power. They wanted My Mistress, but she was mine.

'Get your own!' I'd blaze.

My doctor made me see sense the other day. He told me: 'Give Stella up. Your liver can't take any more.'

The Mistress   *Amy Rafferty*

And then we woke up, shook cigarettes from their packs. You lit mine, placed it between my lips. I always hated that. You couldn't look at me. We drank coffee in silence and you coughed, no hand over your mouth. You had known me too long.

I asked, 'Is there a call you should be making?'

You stood then and reached for the phone, but I choked in the moment and took it from your hands, led you back to bed. You here in the morning was inevitable, the desired outcome of my plans.

At least, I had thought so.

The Mistress   *Steven Schusman*

My wife accepts it.

She is years younger than my wife; it is a different relationship altogether. She makes no demands of me: she never rings me, she does not require me to listen, she harbours no jealousy. She has no family, no shame (nor do I), no responsibilities and no inhibitions. She is hedonism personified. She turns heads without trying, yet is completely devoid of vanity. Her perfect, toned, sleek body and soft eyes are irresistible. I cannot help myself. I love her despite her single-mindedness.

Yet when my wife, the mistress, instructs her to sit, she sits.

The Mistress   *Jenni Doherty*

Eight pounds, three ounces she was, and so beautiful: a shock of curly red hair, smooth porcelain skin and rose-petalled cheeks. He could hold her in the palm of his hand, her chubby little fingers opening up like a lily. And her face, oh, her face, was exactly how he had imagined angels to look, and with the bluest of eyes. Like little stars they were. She even had the scent of flowers on her soft skin. She was all Danny's. His own creation. A little piece of heaven, and he would keep his word: he'd tell the wife.

The Next Stage   *Perry Gretton*

'I want y'all on the next stagecoach outta here,' said Sheriff Stevens, 'or I'll pump yer so full o' lead they'll need a locomotive to drag yer bodies to Boot Hill.'

'But we ain't done nothin' wrong,' said Billy. 'Me and the boys were just actin' kinda friendly to all you good folk.'

'Sure. My deputy's resigned, the mayor's in hidin', and Belle deVille and her girls have hightailed it outta town. Very friendly.'

'Aw, come on, Sheriff. That was just a coincidence.'

'Sure as hell it was. And don't forget to take all them goddamn bibles with yer.'

The Next Stage   *Lynda Kenny*

I travelled to see my great-great-grandmother on her Death Day, 18 January 2031. When I arrived in that ancient, shattered land, the sky was the all-too-familiar flame red.

We were only allowed to visit our relatives on their Death Days. It was the law, to ensure we did not interfere with the timeline protocol. Most of us chose to do this; it enabled us to bring some little comfort to them, the last of the corporeal beings.

Sometimes fear and ignorance made them plead for the old ways, but we explained gently that we had evolved.

165

The Next Stage
Karen Jones

It's been three months. I followed the "rules": didn't sleep with him until the third date, never called, let him do the running. It worked. I've moved some of my stuff into his bathroom – discreetly. It's the next stage.

I love him.

* * * *

It's been three months. She was easy: in bed by the third date. Good fun, though. Now I'm in love.

The new girl calls and texts all the time – it's a real turn on. Ready for the next stage. I'll have to get rid of the other one first. She'll be okay; she knows the rules.

The Next Stop
Shonali Bhattacharya

She sat on a stool at the far, dark end of the bar, corrugated thoughts covering the hinges in the forehead. The bar girl served me whiskey, added three cubes of ice, cleared the ashtray, followed my stare, smiled. Her face lit up to a John Denver, motionless; grip cringed on the drink, chin up to make rings of smoke, stare sharp as dried grass blade.

Another time, another man, same mistake, she told herself: *am again running faster than dreams can die.*

I took my whiskey, walked up to her, the solitary maiden, now drowned in clouds of smoke.

The Operation
Perry Gretton

Debbie never tired of talking about her operation. After all, it had been a real operation – an appendectomy – not something cosmetic.

Adam no longer listened and either nodded or muttered

some inanity while he read his newspaper or watched TV. He contemplated telling her about his visit to the doctor, then thought better of it. What he had was inoperable.

The Picture   *Nicky Philips*
Camilla felt warm affection for her Victorian grandmother as she collected her from the picture restorer. As an artist, she had always loved that picture for both its style and subject. The restorer had discovered a letter behind the backing from the artist to her grandmother. So they were lovers. Reading on, Camilla realised the origin of her artistic talent!

The Playroom   *Colin Biggs*
A thousand times over I searched for the hidden days. Sometimes through the darkness I could see the playroom, the toys neatly stored on shelves. But nothing more; no child laughing within. At my own child's eighth birthday party, he tried to assert his growing personality, foolishly defying me in front of his friends. I hid my shock and pain quite well, I thought, but after they left, I punched the lesson into him. I glared down at him, and when I saw the blood from his mouth mixing with his tears, I finally remembered my time in the playroom.

The Playroom   *Steven Schusman*
Every content was devoted to peals and squeals, merriment and mirth. Gaily painted surfaces adorned with tantalising creations of the imagination contributed to a quarter primed for play. The latest gadgets lay scattered amongst more traditional artefacts lovingly carved from now outlawed hardwoods. No such room would be complete without table-tennis bats, yet no table. A swing was suspended from the crossbeams in the middle, but

the boys and girls still loved to amuse themselves thereon, just as they would have done in their childhood. Mirrored walls and ceiling, plus waterbed were, of course, *de rigueur*.

The Race   *Carolyn Roberts*

He threw the car into the last corner, hardly touching the brakes. Wheels squealing, he flattened the accelerator and tore down the final straight. He couldn't have done it any faster, but had it been quick enough?

The nurse looked at him ruefully. 'Sorry, Mister Martin, I'm afraid you missed the birth. But you have a lovely new baby boy!'

The Race   *Gavin Damerell*

Impressed by his modesty, the headlines simply read, *I'm Just Lucky*.

He'd done it: he'd won gold and set a new world record. He was now a national hero – a hero held up to inspire future generations of athletes to train hard, to strive for seemingly impossible dreams. But most importantly, for himself to stay quiet about performance-enhancing drugs.

The Race   *Anatoly Kudryavitsky*

The jungle is an entanglement of tails. There are scores of animals there, and their tails form a web, a better one than those woven by spiders. Pink plastic babies make their way through a thicket, all in one direction. Over their heads, a golden arrow glares in the sky, as well as bright images of Darwin and TH Huxley.

(Translated from the Russian by the author.)

The Right Decision   *Gavin Damerell*

My eyes consume it all yet take in nothing. So I try to stay calm, composed.

'Think,' I say to myself, 'think!' I almost scream. But I can't concentrate, as now they're all watching me, making me nervous – and for such an important decision, too!

I have only one choice . . .

'Chicken Tikka Masala, please,' I stammer.

The Silent Pool   *Gavin Parish*

It was our secret, our discovery. We came here as kids, Andy and me. The old place had a peaceful serenity, disturbed only by our playful laughter, echoing back at us from the quarry walls. We stripped to our swim shorts and raced to be first into the fresh, cool water.

I broke the surface alone, instantly aware that something was wrong. My frantic, drawn-out search proved fruitless. Later, the police divers turned up nothing, either.

I still come here occasionally, though the waters seem darker and the laughter is just a memory. All that remains is the silent pool.

The Silent Pool   *Colin Biggs*

The wretched beggar woman pleaded. I laughed at her, carelessly tossing a twenty into her lap. I wouldn't miss it. She reached out, her smell strong as she pulled me close to her; strangely, not foul, but fresh as forest dawn.

'Do you remember the pool, Giles?' she whispered, 'and the drink that you took?'

Shaking at her words, I became the youth once more, naked in the wooded valley where the silent pool lay shrouded by mist. I looked into her beautiful eyes, remembering our love, and her pale sweet body.

'Is it time to drink again?' I asked.

The Silent Pool — *Estelle Kirk*

With bare feet, Kerys trod the path up towards the Withy Pool. She held her face stony calm until she reached the clearing and sat on a rock. Then unstoppable tears ran down her cheeks.

Her fingers were red-raw from her chores – her back ached from lifting and carrying – but it was her heart that hurt the most. It seemed as if the reeds stopped swaying and even the blackbirds hushed with tilted heads to listen.

'Mother, I love you and miss you,' she whispered to the silent pool. It was the only place she could tell her troubles.

The Source — *Lynda Kenny*

When she stretched out her arm to clasp the sword, her kind stepped away from human view. Fairy rings lay empty and unicorns disappeared from the land. Avalon, Tír na Óg and Shangri-La moved into legend. Deemed too coarse to understand the gentleness of magic, mankind was left alone, bereft of wonder, and with a yearning it could never fulfil.

The Source — *Kevin Connolly*

'To make an omelette,' the old man replied to his grandson's joke, 'you've first got to break a few eggs. Unless you have a beginning, there can be no end; without a source, there's no destination; without cause, no effect. Before the chicken can cross the road, an almighty, omnipotent being first has to create the universe.'

The Source   *Karen Jones*

The surgery went on longer than they'd expected. The anaesthetist voiced his concern: the patient was vastly overweight, not the ideal candidate for a lengthy operation. The surgeon prodded and probed but still couldn't reach the source of the problem. Finally, he felt it. There was a snip followed by a twang.

'Got it,' he sighed. Another thong-ectomy successfully completed.

The Source   *Darren Wheatley*

For many years, I shunned the baying crowd, choosing instead to bury myself in study. Slowly, over time, I carefully peeled back the layers of history, until finally, the secrets of the ancients were revealed to me. Now you, too, can share my discovery. Simply send a cheque for twenty-five pounds and soon, you'll be satisfying your partner the Celtic way.

The Tape   *Karen Jones*

He listened to the evidence that would end his career. Stupid: he should have been more careful. Hell, he'd given them the authority to bug; he'd just never expected it to backfire so spectacularly.

Sitting back, taking a final look around the office, he knew there'd been some good work done here, some real progress, some success. His name, his legacy would live on; this little slip-up would soon be forgotten. One day, he'd be a legend. A smile softened President Richard Nixon's lips.

'Does my voice really sound like that? I'll never get used to hearing myself on tape.'

The Tape   *Perry Gretton*

Frank Gibson cut the tape and the crowd surged forward onto the new bridge. As the mayor was saying, 'Thank you, Frank, for everything you've done,' they heard a scream, followed by frantic shouting. Frank, hesitating only briefly, sprinted to the river, removed his jacket and shoes, and plunged in.

It was late when he drove home from the hospital. His wife was waiting for him on the doorstep.

'It was her, wasn't it?'

She tried blocking his path, but he pushed past her and entered the house.

She screamed at his retreating back, 'You promised me, you lying bastard!'

The Vanishing Words   *Eileen Burzynska*

I happened to chance upon the *Pulsating Flesh* website. The screen throbbed black and red like a putrid wound and would not let me go. No Exit, no Close, no Escape.

'Help!' I keyed. 'Help!' scoring into the mess like a butcher's knife. Blood dripped over the words and onto the keyboard. The monitor faded to black and then died.

The Vanishing Words   *Jill Paiton*

His betrayal had left her emotions drained and in tatters. She had revealed a sacred part of herself to him: her soul. She lamented letting her defences down with someone so shallow and clichéd. To allow oneself such liberal vulnerability she now saw as a major flaw. Victory flooded her psyche as the laser removed his name from her arm.

The Vanishing Words   *Robert Capps*

Words heard all our lives, words that make us alive, whispered in dark corners, hidden behind nasty black lies. Words felt deep within hearts when all is so quiet. Words we see when they flare in our heads – all of them cannot be lost or mislaid. Listening to sounds all around, words can't be the only company when dead.

The Vanishing Words   *Darren Wheatley*

Adrian Palmer stepped up to the lectern, staring down the capacity crowd, ready to make the speech of his life. He risked everything; no turning back once they felt the weight of his words. With a powerful hand gesture, he held them all in the palm of his unwavering hand. Destiny engulfed him. The room hung in breathless anticipation. Then . . .

The Wall   *Mark Burns*

Each day when I face it, I reflect on Buddhist wisdom. A journey begins with a single step.

It reminds me of my father. I saw him as a magician, a wizard, a dream maker. Day after day, he laid brick upon brick and created reality from mortar and stone. From nothing and from the ground up he built homes, towers, hospitals, schools – even a prison. His life was building walls.

Each day I face my own. There's no way over, under, around. So I go through it. It's paper thin, blank, white.

Punch through it, write the first word.

The Wall   *Teri Davis-Rouvelas*

Becky and fiancé Peter chose the house that spring for its impressive driveway, which led straight from the stonewall-edged street to their front doorstep. Summer shone happy through the elms lining the lane, yet autumn was a haze seen through her suspicious tears.

But it was winter that took her breath away: bare branches like ink slashes on unsent invitations.

The car's heater blew the wedding veil from her eyes. A note to Peter and his new bride rested under her gown's train as Becky pressed the gas pedal to the floor for one final, stony kiss.

The Weekend — *Lee Henderson*

'Will she bring my present, Daddy?' Karen asked, squeezing my hand, small face lit-up in anticipation.

'Yeah, of course she will, precious,' I answered. *Even my Ex wouldn't forget her only daughter's birthday, surely?*

Come the weekend, no sign of card or a call. Sunday. Sobbing.

'Why didn't Mummy come, Daddy?' Karen's tears killed lingering doubts.

The Weekend — *Julieann Campbell*

Finally. Head held high, she files her papers away and leaves the stuffy office with a spring in her step – another triumph over unemployment. With fresh odour of uninspiring antique cream paint finally leaving her nostrils, she beams widely, at last! Glowing, eager at the thought of what's to come, she strolls on. Hazy nights, dawn too soon. Bliss.

Thirst — *Kevin Connolly*

I was dying for a hair of the dog.

'I'm sorry but I'm gagging for a drink,' I said to the smarmy young lady who had come to inquire why I hadn't paid the

Council Tax on my castle. 'Do you mind if I quench my thirst before the interrogation commences?'

'Not at all,' she replied. 'Drink away, Count Dracula.'

Thirst   *Lynda Kenny*

Oh, I had such a thirst for you, a deep, soul-quenching thirst for you. To kiss you was to drink an ocean dry. To touch, absorb you from every pore. Rapacious, ravenous, bittersweet. But time slakes all thirsts, feeds all hungers, flattens mountains of emotion, and dulls even the sharpest of pains. So, I never saw you again.

Thirst   *Amanda Mair*

This thirst was unquenchable. It consumed him night and day. He tried; he thought he really had tried. He avoided places, people.

Was it his fault, then, when this boy appeared while he was parked, waiting on a desolate road? A young boy, alone, riding his bike. No-one around. His thirst for another's life-blood absorbed, then satiated him for the moment.

Thirst   *Clarissa Henry*

An insatiable thirst for knowledge drove him through sleepless nights. Book after book, none could quench the inner fire. A pretty girl turned the old sage away from his quest. He prayed for youth and love requited. The Devil heard his plea, granted him love and knowledge in exchange for his soul. In hell, nothing can slake his eternal thirst.

Time   *Karen Jones*

I look at the faded faces: images caught on camera, almost un-recognisable to me now. I used to know them, play with them, love them . . . envy them. Now they're just snapshots of an-other life. Ghosts from the past haunting my fragile memory.

And that beautiful girl – was that me?

I peer through the fog over the valley, my daily search for signs of life. It's a forlorn hope. Many years have passed since I last saw another human face – or even an animal's face.

The mirror records the relentless march of wrinkles, sags and liver spots on my own countenance, yet I can't bring myself to break it. So few things survived after the explosions, it would be sacrilege to wantonly destroy possessions.

I allow myself a smile –"wanton destruction" would be syn-onymous with my name, if there was anyone left to record my life. The first female president, the one who pushed the button, the one who made a pact to defy death. Now time and death defy me.

Time   *Perry Gretton*

Gerald boarded the bus and handed his fare to the driver. She looked him over and said, 'You know the *Doctor Who* conven-tion doesn't start till tomorrow, don't you?'

'Of course.'

He found a window seat and took out his well-thumbed copy of *Doctor Who and the Daemons*. He became so engrossed in the story that he almost missed his stop.

At the convention centre, he approached the entrance and leisurely studied the large posters on the doors. Turning away, he heard an unearthly pulsating sound and an old police box materialised before him. Its door opened and out stepped Doc-tor Who. He gave a cheery wave to Gerald before peering at the posters.

'Oh, dear, seems like I'm a day early. Never could get this thing to work properly.'

'I know. You're a bugger to emulate.'

'I'll give it another go,' said the Doctor, returning to the TARDIS. A moment later, the box disappeared.

Gerald sat on a nearby bench and pulled out his book. Within seconds, he was absorbed by the story again.

Time   *Nina Simon*

Ignoring "Warning – Demolition" signs, Jeanette picked her way over broken glass, bricks and discarded rubbish. Cautiously, she entered her former home.

Why did I come? she wondered. Yet something drew her in. She crossed the rubble-filled hallway. The lounge was lit only by the few rays of sunlight infiltrating gaps in the boarded-up windows. Dust coated every surface.

She collapsed onto a chair thoughtfully left in the corner. *I'm in as bad a state as this house. Time hasn't been kind to either of us.* She closed her eyes. Larry was in front of her, smiling.

'Larry, my love,' she whispered, moving into his outstretched arms.

* * * *

The bulldozer crashed over the front garden. Its driver braked and climbed down.

'Won't be long, Bert,' Jim shouted, 'I left my mobile inside yesterday.'

A short while later, he ran out of the house, shouting madly.

'What's up, Jim? You seen a ghost?' Bert joked.

'Almost,' Jim replied. 'There's an old woman in there. I think she's dead.'

Time   *Hazel Buckingham*

He told her: 'Remember – seven-thirty . . . or I won't be there.'

With the light dimming, the birds sang the last of their songs from heavily blossomed trees. She smiled. The place looked the same: the wheel-worn, shiny cobbles in the market-place still reflected the orange sunset and the church spire still stabbed awkwardly at the sky. She lifted her skirts and walked towards this landmark. Her footsteps, now a panicked run, as the chimes began striking the half-hour. She must be on time. This opportunity would never occur again.

A shadow smeared the oak lych-gate.

'Edward! My love, my destiny. The magic you taught me served me well. Despite fate trying its hardest to keep us apart through these centuries, I have arrived on time . . . Take me.'

He wrapped his cloak around her. On the last stroke of seven-thirty, he lifted her face to his and kissed in her soul. Their spirits united, at last.

Time of Death   *Richard Chalu*

The crane lowered the Granada into the crusher. Muffled cries could just be heard over the roaring machinery. From his cabin, Dave noticed a rope-tied hand clawing the car window. *Shit,* he thought, jumping from his seat. Passing the crusher's open jaws, he glimpsed the gagged Armenian's panicked, pleading eyes. Dave sighed and checked his watch as the crusher began its work: 8.15pm. His lucrative sideline was becoming less palatable. Before long, a metal block was spat from the machine, several fissures gently oozing blood. Grabbing the pressure washer, he vowed this would be the last immigrant he "helped" into Britain.

Time of Death *Roy Weltman*

Her mutilated body lay withered in the reservoir, her eyes staring accusingly at the men standing around her necropolis. The coroner said time of death was between 2.00am and 4.00am. Detective Sergeant Riley knew it to be at 3.00am exactly. As he covered her body, he thought about his promise and knew he had failed her. It was finally over.

Time of Death *Colin Biggs*

The old woman's chanting, usually so comforting, instead irritated, filling my darkness with fleeting, shameful images. Unattended, the slumbering brazier smoked lazily, comfortless, cruel in its glowing gaze, impotent against the coldness seeping through the dripping stone walls. Each of us there, broken, weeping like children, fought to forget the pain and fear, each unable to face the image of our day to come and our own final journey. The old woman shuddered to silence, her spine finally cracked as the great wheel edged another notch forward. A blessed release. The Jesuit grinned at us as he prepared his instruments.

Time of Death *Petya Mihaylova Stefanova-Gieridis*

'Here's your room, Rose, decorated in your colours. The new polychrome therapy does wonders. No white walls and sheets anymore! White is the colour of death. Ah, look at the windows – there are no bars! You bad girl! You know books are banned! Reading impedes recovery!'

Ignorance is a blissful condition, isn't it, John? Let's walk on the thin ice.

'Here's your room, Lily, decorated in your colour. The new monochrome therapy . . .'

Lily came closer to the window and touched the freshly

painted white bars. Below, in the garden, the earth was embracing the last dead rose petals.

To Kill a Dead Man   *Darren Wheatley*

The doctors seemed to think it was a good thing that he might "live" at least two more years. I gazed at the frail, hacking sack of bones, the mortal remains of the man who used to carry me without effort atop his broad shoulders, and I broke inside.

I knew I'd done the right thing when he didn't struggle.

To Kill a Dead Man   *Shirley Bunyan*

She stared, transfixed, at the blurred newspaper image of a crumpled figure in the street. 'Self-defence,' the police said. 'Sorry, it was unavoidable. He was armed and dangerous.'

She wasn't sorry. He'd only existed in the blackest of nights, the deepest of terrors. She wanted to tell them they hadn't killed him – couldn't have. He'd been dead for years.

To Kill a Dead Man   *Karen Jones*

When she left, she took my heart, squeezed it dry, cast it aside. When she left, she took every ounce of hope, every grain of desire, every drop of love. Every moment since has seemed eternal, every task futile, every memory filled with her passion's poison.

In the mirror, I see a dead man – he's just too weak to die.

To Kill a Dead Man   *Maureen Wilkinson*

'Get lost, it's over,' he said.

Libby looked into his arrogant face. She wanted to gouge out the cold, unfeeling eyes, plunge a knife into his callous heart and rip out the merciless tongue. He was devoid of feeling, so how could she kill a man already dead. Her fists beat an ineffectual tattoo on his chest.

Tombstones and Trinkets　　　　　　　*Darren Wheatley*

'Earth to earth . . .'

'Look at 'em all, rubbing their hands.'

'. . . Ashes to ashes.'

'I reckon they'll have a price tag on everything in that house by now.'

'. . . Dust to dust.'

'Well, they're not getting their hands on the Ormolu clock!'

'. . . The Lord bless her and keep her.'

'Promised me that herself, she did.'

'. . . The Lord make her face to shine upon her.'

'Just before she choked on that sausage roll.'

'. . . And be gracious unto her.'

'I remember it well, it were at Queenie's wake, last week.'

'. . . And give her peace.'

'Left me some lovely Wedgewood, did Queenie.'

'Amen.'

'Amen.'

Tombstones and Trinkets　　　　　　*Christopher Spalding*

Carol emerged from the early morning mist. The headphones clamped to her ears gave the appearance of an alien recently alighted from some fantastic craft; electronic sounding bleeps periodically cut through the soft, persistent patter of drizzle on stone.

At the church, Carol stopped abruptly as if challenged by the sheer arrogance of the architecture. She turned, staring back across a legion of dispassionate headstones, and knelt down.

Scraping at the dewy grass, she unearthed a small gold cross on a broken chain.

'Nothing here,' she sighed, 'only tombstones and trinkets.' She packed the metal detector back into her car.

Tombstones and Trinkets   *Estelle Kirk*

The azure sky stretched peacefully down until it became an azure sea. An island of smooth sand lay like a pool of gold, but it was troubled by shouts from a game. Salt-stained men ran helter-skelter, kicking and hurling an ungainly ball that they had made themselves. One end of the beach was marked by two palm trees; the other by two hasty gravestones. The ball left a trail of pearls, like tears from its eyes. For it was a skull, weighted with gold and jewels. Whoever won this game of "tombstones and trinkets" was to eat the ship's last biscuit.

Tomorrow's Headlines   *Darren Wheatley*

As he entered the station, he fought the urge to smile at the CCTV camera staring down on him, suppressed a sneer as the credit-card reader logged his ticket purchase, and barely contained his disdain at the perfunctory security inspection. In his mind, he knew what the papers would say. His heart told him it would never be enough.

Tomorrow's Headlines   *Moses Abukutsa*

The deadly weapons sprayed all for the cameras in the slums. All the youth up in arms against crime, against the evils of their friends, against police gunning innocent youth. Hundreds dead, hundreds homeless, millions starving south of the Sahara – those are tomorrow's headlines. All of us are writing them in our selfish ink all over the world.

Trace *Karen Jones*

Softly, she touched his face with her fingertips then let them slip to his chest, his quick breath pushing against her caress. Leaning forward, she kissed his forehead and gently laid him down. During the fights, sulks and recriminations of the future, she'd keep this picture mapped out in her mind. The only trace left of her perfect, unspoilt child.

Trace *Lee Henderson*

The old lab lay in the doorway, head resting on crossed paws.

'Geez, Trace, do you always have to lay there?' he asked, stepping over the dog.

Then it struck him: four years since Ginny died. Our little girl. She used to sit there and scratch him. Tears came as he looked down.

'Stay, girl, there's a good dog.'

Turned Down *Perry Gretton*

'I said get off me!' I twisted and squirmed until I was out of his grip. 'Leave me alone!'

He looked bemused. 'But none of the other girls mind.'

'Don't they? You bet they do. They're just desperate to keep their jobs.'

'Well, now you've lost yours.'

'Have I? In that case . . .'

And I kicked him hard in the balls.

Turned Down *Jenni Doherty*

I wanted to confess to her, on that wasted luxury of silken morn, all the stories of where I'd been: those bloody cities and death-filled towns. I wanted to tell of the shattered men, their children dead, how they had begged of me to save them.

I looked at her, so pure and white, my wife-to-be, and said, 'I can't.'

Turned Down   *Miriam Heinbuch*

So now, once again, she found herself standing in front of his door. She always used to find herself there, after every escape, every single adventure.

Every time, like by a magic hand of fate, he used to open it. She would walk through it, knowing in the back of her mind that this scene would repeat itself, possibly until the end of time. But not this time. This time, she would go inside, and she would stay.

So now, once again, she found herself standing in front of his door. This time it would remain closed. For good.

Turning the Corner   *Julie Okon*

She stalled the damned thing six times in less than ten minutes. She was getting more and more flustered; his Cockney tones, with a touch of self-parody, calmed her, revealed to her the milliard secrets of a clutch's control. She started the engine; smoothly slid into second . . .

'Ahh, there you are. Now we're turning the corner.'

Turning the Corner   *Shonali Bhattacharya*

Where the river has meandered, there straight ahead, where the sky becomes bigger, Abu Chacha brings his boat, anchors it in the knee-deep mud. There, where a small lamp glows, is his hut. He takes home his catch. Aasma Bou will cook dinner now: rice and crab curry. The wood is wet, she will use the kerosene stove today.

Turning the Page   *Annie Bien*

He writes "Autobiography". He turns blank pages, unmarred with thought, untouched by ink, counts leaves, turns to page 216. The nib touches paper: page 216. Eighty-four pages 'til the end of my life. She still remains to the left of my right hand wrapped around my back – unreachable. Polar ice caps, like kneecaps, lose cartilage. Glacial sea: bone-chilling, not quite drowning; I slip, regain toeholds. The last pages remain unwritten because autobiographies can only be completed while alive; they're never finished. If they end, so do I. By burning page 300, my outcome is uncertain, disallowing hindsight.

Under Cover   *Karen Jones*

The walls retained the history of the house: not just its energy, its origins. Each craftsman had signed his name on the newly plastered walls, including Eddie's predecessor, Fred Graham, 1910.

As his float glided over the last ghost, he felt the house shiver; history had been obliterated for a smooth finish. His signature would feel like a confession.

Under Cover   *Jenni Doherty*

You were there. I could feel you inside but I couldn't tell them. I couldn't tell him – the shame, the disgust, the fear. I booked a return ticket to London. It was two days before my birthday. I was nineteen.

'Visiting friends,' I'd said. 'Just for the weekend. Will bring you back something.'

And I did: my empty womb.

Under Cover   *Eileen Burzynska*

You lean back, relishing the comfort of your chair, watching your television programme through half-closed eyes. Lifting the mug to your lips, you drink your coffee with a contented sigh and replace it on the side table. You look up and smile and hold out your hand, warm and dry. I have been observing you for over thirty years.

Under the Bridge   *Shirley Bunyan*

The relentless dripping echoed a macabre lullaby. Her hands ached, straining to keep their grip on the wet rock as exhaustion crept in. Pure terror had subsided hours ago for a black dread rapidly choking any spark of hope. Her whimpering faded into the dark as she struggled to remember how she had slipped into this pit of hell. They had warned her.

'Don't go under the bridge. Never go under the bridge.'

But the compulsion was too strong. How she'd ached to share her secret. She loved him. He loved her. She knew it. The three of them would be so happy together.

'Meet me tonight, seven o'clock, under the bridge.'

His eyes had simmered with . . . passion . . . yes, passion.

She'd made her way, heart pounding, to the rendezvous, never stopping to wonder why, this time, he hadn't told her to go away and leave him alone.

Under the Bridge   *Moses Abukutsa*

The sun shone and was conspicuously reflected on the surface of the snaking river. Orman, the orphan, looking into the river with thoughts full in his little mind. The teenager looked at his image in the water and tears trickled down his eyelids. He was not going to give himself another chance of humiliation before his venomous stepmother back home. He strolled down the riverbank, watching the high bridge. The determined spirit in him moved his heavy feet, his father was not home, but to him, even father was foe. The sound of thunderous water against rocks aroused him and at that moment, he hurled himself into the river. As the river swept him away towards the bridge, he buried his head deep into the water. And under the bridge, he vanished.

Under the Bridge   *Mark Burns*

His car, a '94 Fiesta, was left, hazard lights blinking, engine running and radio playing, on the city-bound lane.

It was way past midnight when the police came to the door and by then, the rescue call had already been out for over an hour. Weekend volunteers in their fluorescent jackets and with flashlights beaming and their radios crackling patrolled both banks. A motorboat streamed the outgoing tide.

By morning, local fishermen in their skiffs and rowboats had joined the search. We prayed hard and drank tea by the gallon, though we knew that when someone went in, they rarely came out. The local paper proclaimed him missing. No proof yet, but the wind whispered, 'No choice, presume him dead.'

He surfaced after nine days, disfigured, bloated. Our family's singular victim, but another notch on a rising tally. No way out: succumb, jump from the bridge.

Under the Bridge   *Darren Anderson*

The kids were messing around under the bridge when they found it. A briefcase with a combination lock. They tried a few numbers, then gave up and bashed it in with a rock. And there it was, plain as day. Seven hundred thousand in used bank notes. One of them started jumping up and down; another was giggling; a third sat open-mouthed. Two of them started dancing, laughing, their mouths running off in circles about how they'd spend it.

'Wait!' said one of the older ones, 'no-one can find out about this. Right? You all have to swear never to tell anyone. We'll have to hide it and spend it later.'

So they did. And they knew nothing, nor would they ever know, about the kidnapping. Or the ransom. Or the drop-off spot. Or Catherine, who, during the next few weeks, was sent through the post. Piece by piece.

Under the Influence   *Stephen Reilly*

I was living in a B&B in Bristol, she in our flat in Putney. We were separated.

I sat in a train after work on my way to marriage guidance in London, my career the source of our problems. My mobile rang. My boss wanted me back in the office.

She didn't show up.

Back in Bristol, I worked all night.

Under the Influence   *Corey Evans*

I followed her from the woods in the west to the steaming city in the east. She moved often; her job demanded it. I was a writer; I could work from anywhere. Maybe she didn't even like me, but I was persistent. Whenever she left, I had to go find her. The smell of her perfume intoxicating, removing my inhibitions.

Under the Palm   *Elizabeth Madden*

Under the palm, six prisoners: one female, five male – two black, one brown, three white. Qa'id approaches.

'You believe in democracy, huh? Here's the deal: three die, three live. You get to vote – pretty fair, no?'

They look at each other, hesitating . . .
'So, no democracy? Let me decide for you.'
Qa'id shoots.

Under the Palm   *Jill Paiton*

Skye would spend summer holidays in exile under the palm's
generous shade. The graceful encompassing arms of the tree's
ample green leaves provided vital protection and sanctuary to
spend in pursuit of her favourite pastime: the rapture of daydreaming. This luxurious pleasure was often abruptly jolted
by the abrasive sounds of her parents screaming and shouting
abuse in the kitchen.

Under the Palm   *Perry Gretton*

Lying languidly in a hammock strung between two palms, piña
colada in hand, lost in a daydream, I heard my mobile ring.

'Jenkins has just resigned and I need you back here immediately.'

'But, boss, I'm on holiday—'

'Not any more, you're not. Get your arse on the first plane
out of there.'

Such is one's life under the palm.

Underwear   *Darren Wheatley*

Kieran frowned into his beer and rued his rotten luck with the
ladies. All week he'd worn his lucky boxers and still wasn't getting
a sniff. Slurping dregs, he resolved to go home and change.

Rushing back into town for Happy Hour, he missed the
Number 37.

It didn't miss him.

At least his mother would've approved of his pants.

Underwear   *Carolyn Roberts*

The notices appeared overnight in every major city:

ATTENTION! In light of recent unpleasant incidents, which frankly have put the Prime Minister right off his morning muffins, parliament has passed the Attractive Underwear Act 2006. Anyone found with tatty, unwashed or otherwise undesirable underwear visible over the top of their trousers will be subject to an on-the-spot fine of £200.

Vein Glorious   *Fionnuala McGowan*

Very handsome, she thought, watching the boy.

'Anvil? Sickle? Dark Angel?' they shouted.

'Not bad,' he smiled.

The game was novel, she supposed, if a little puerile.

'Our glorious Soviet Republic!' shouted Sergei triumphantly.

'Good, comrade, but too conventional. I need originality,' said the boy.

'The South Eastern United States of America?' a small voice ventured.

As the jeers erupted, she came before him. Gently she ran her fingers across the silk of his scalp, caressing his mysterious mark with gossamer grace. Heat stirred in his loins as she worked her way along the definition of his birth. Silence throbbed in the room.

'So,' he said, his voice teasing, inviting, 'you have an answer?'

'A bleeding chicken?' she smiled disarmingly.

He threw back his head, roaring with laughter. 'Excellent, comrade, you win. What is your name?'

'Raisa,' she said. 'And yours?'

'Mikhail,' he said, stretching forth his hand.

Waterfall   *Annie Bien*

A trail of tiny bubbles, esses tumble in light – a pebble falls
– marsh-grass blades curve and reshape like strands of tossed
hair from a woman's face; a wide-eyed fish curves a round-
mouthed gasp and fins by. Down I drift, aswirl with dirt cloud
from mud embraced. Water settles. I see my face age in ripples.
An illusory life.

Waterfall   *Corey Evans*

Under the cascade, the children played. Balancing on the rocks,
dipping small feet into chilly waters. The sound almost deafen-
ing, she couldn't hear the scream as the smaller one slipped and
slid. Hanging on by torn fingernails against the raging torrent,
the boy grew tired and released.

The older one shouted again, 'Papa!'

A firm, strong hand saved the day.

We Are Not Alone   *Eileen Burzynska*

Entwined, we quietly leave the party, sliding through shadows
into the garden. Distant music fades, replaced by the rustling
of dark leaves; candle glow gives way to starlight glimmering
down from a hundred light years. The threatening beauty of
the night closes around us and I shiver. Beneath our blanket, a
thousand little unsuspected lives unfold. We are not alone.

We Are Writing to You Because . . .   *Andrew Clark*

We are writing to you to apologise. Forgive us. Remember the
early days, the first gigs. Nu-rave, they called it, but it wasn't
just that – it was a nu-*ravolution*. Magic, wasn't it?

We got older. How could we not? And success corrupts, we
see that now. The adverts were a mistake. The concept album.

The collaborations with "world artistes".

We're writing to promise we've changed. No more drugs or ballads. Let this album sleeve be testament to that. We have changed to what we were before. We're writing to say we love you. After all, you pay the bills, suckers!

We Are Writing to You Because . . . *Hazel Buckingham*

'We have Nobby. We'll ring at two.'

Derek studied the cut-out newspaper letters. Sure enough, at two . . .

'Ten million and we'll release him.'

'Yeah, right.'

Click . . . Ten minutes later:

'Don't call the police. Five million.'

'What? Aren't you supposed to raise the ransom?'

'Nobby'll get something chopped off . . .'

'Go ahead.'

'One million.'

'Yeah, 'course.'

Click . . . Ten minutes later:

'Nobby's not happy. Look on your doormat . . .'

'You disgusting pervert. How could you do that?'

'Half a million for Nobby's return.'

'Piss off!'

'Quarter of a million.'

'No.'

'Thought you loved Nobby?'

'I do, but those gnomes only cost two quid!'

What's It Worth? *Dan Purdue*

It was one just like hers.

The bow-tied man droned on and on.

'What's it worth?' she yelled at the telly. 'What's it worth?'

She clapped her hands and stamped her feet when he said. The cat hid under the sideboard.

In the kitchen, her husband swiftly dust-panned the fragments into the bin. *Surely she wouldn't miss that old thing . . .*

What's It Worth? *Nicky Philips*

To me, it's priceless. It was given to me by my parents the day I was born: 1 April 1980. Children at primary school stood in awe of it: it helped immensely through college; as an adult, I never leave home without it. It's right there, in my pocket by the door key and credit card: my precious, invaluable sense of humour.

Where Did It Go? *Anne Rainbow*

As Jake slumped onto her bare breasts, breathing sweet nothings, Katherine realised summer was over.

Was it only yesterday she'd sensed the subtle shift from spring? The novelty of their relationship evaporating like a morning mist burnt off in the sunshine? They'd shared glorious times; love had blossomed. Yet, he took her for granted.

Today, autumn arrived and she shivered.

Where Did It Go? *Jenni Doherty*

When I met her, I knew: two souls in fast recognition. It was an uncanny sensation. We were confused but excited as we absorbed each other. She was glorious, stubborn, an extrovert. Her honey-milk skin, her eyes bright brown moon-tilts. Pure gold. Our bodies, minds entwined, in rhythm, as one. God, how I loved her . . .

'I'm sorry, James. She's gone.'

Whispers *Lee Henderson*

Captain Brian Hennessy, late of the Australian Iraqi Expeditionary Force, lay sweating in the infirmary's bed, mumbling, 'I can't, I can't!'

In his mind, decapitated heads whispered to him: pain, betrayal, fear, disgust. Whispers changed to terrified screams. Flashing blades.

'Captain, please! Captain, tell them! Captain! Please!'

'I can't! My orders, I can't,' he sobbed.

Whispers *Stephen Reilly*

On nights such as these, when a northeasterly lashes the cove like then, she visits me. I leave a light in the window and huddle by the fire, counting the minutes until I sense her shadow at the sill. I will tell her again how I love her and pray she may whisper, 'Come, Papa, to my grave beneath the sea.'

Whispers *Karen Jones*

He strokes her back, her shoulders, her arms. His glances find her cold blue eyes. Trembling fingers run through her hair; moist lips find her throat; smooth hands long to seek her breasts. Stopping, waiting, he takes a deep breath, whispers the question.

'Yes,' she murmurs. He smiles, shudders – even though he knew it was a foregone financial conclusion.

White Noise *Amanda Mair*

He dragged me into an abandoned factory.

'Please don't hurt me,' I cried. Ripping my clothes, he forcefully pushed me down and heaved his body onto me. Afterwards, I lay motionless, fearful, yet thankful for life. Tapping, hammering, fashioning and sizzling as sparks danced in darkness.

The forged blade, still white with heat, he drove straight through my heart.

Why? *Perry Gretton*

Why is he watching me? Oh, shit! He's heading towards my counter.
'Can I help you, sir?'

He pulls a card from his pocket and hands it to me. It reads: Sol Joseph. Talent Director. Acme Modelling Agency.

He's waiting for my response. I can't speak. He takes back the card. Before I find my voice, he's walking away.

Why? *Stephen Reilly*

I remember it was blue and made of glass. The ornament sat on a shelf in my parents' bedroom. I lay on their bed one day. I was annoyed, the reason long since forgotten. I was sixteen, the feeling all-consuming. I didn't scream. The ornament shattered into a hundred pieces in front of me. I still don't know why.

Why Did I? *Sarah Star*

It's black and white. I'm signalling ready, but he has to kick the ball to that other prat. And him, he just shrugs! So I squares up to him, right? My face in his. I tells it to him straight, trying to keep it yellow, but he's all bright-red capitals and the sparks are flying. I has to hit him, don't I? Then I'm sent off! Now manager says it's my fault. Chairman's gone and fined me, too. Was only doing them a favour. Ungrateful, I call it. It's enough to make you hit someone. Know what I mean?

Why Did I? *Kitty Redding*

Why did I say that? I replace the receiver and will it to ring, knowing it won't. Unclenching my hands, I persuade myself

– the truth is better said.

Shit, who am I kidding? I pick up the phone – dial – it rings once. I slam it down. Upstairs – reorganise wardrobe – no, not distracting enough. Okay – shoes – coat – then go shopping. Ahh, new top – much better. I peek round the door and my heart skips. The red light is flashing: new message, it screams. With screwed up eyes and a hot face, I press play.

'I love you, too,' he says.

Winning Streak   *Darren Wheatley*

They'd finally done it! Three-one in the final and the ghosts of '66 were finally put to bed. Amid the euphoria on the pitch and off, one man remembered his promise should this day ever occur. Removing his suit, tie, shirt, socks and finally his satin boxers, he ran, arms raised, across the pitch.

'Nice one, Sven!' the crowd roared.

Winning Streak   *Felicity McCall*

'Turn the telly up. She's on now. I've all the neighbours watching. Our Ciara. On *Winning Streak*. Can you credit it? I'd say she'll win the holiday. Even a wee car. They're pure jealous, you know. Hold on! Did you see that, running onto the stage, buck-naked? Shameless hussy; look at her . . . *Ciara?*'

Xtra! Xtra!   *NE Tab Loid*

Transvestite Tory in dramatic sex scandal over footballers' wives orgy with lottery-winner slamming drug-dealing politician in feud with racist hooligan at drunken night out with adulterous single-parent celebrity terrorist besotted with proud teenage ASBO joyrider having tempestuous affair with vigilante alien cult leader in tragic shoot out with masked armed hero police after dog-mauling love nest BB exposé shocker!!! See pages 1-60.

Also: Two million die from Aids in Africa. See page 61, below horoscopes.

The stories you need to hear! Only in your daily newlifemirrorstarsportsunworldtimes!

You Have One New Message   *Karen Jones*

She bought the answering machine when she moved to the city. She recorded a witty message and an amusing piece of music. How they would laugh when they called.

Three weeks of silence followed. Three weeks of staring at the black box, willing it to blink its red flash of popularity. Pride prevented her from calling them. Silence bred depression, despair and finally a solution.

The new message rang out around her slumped, grey, vomit-stained body.

'Jackie, you idiot! You gave everyone the wrong number. Finally got the right one from your new boss. I'm dying to see you.'

You Have One New Message   *Darren Wheatley*

'I know pride is one of the seven, but you can't avoid that sense of smug satisfaction when you get here and it turns out we were right all along.'

'Yeah, I remember thinking the same thing myself, but it turns out everyone was right. Whatever you believe, that's what you get. In other words, atheists get nothing; pagans get Valhalla, and so on. Still up to the "Board" which level you get, though . . .'

'Sorry, I think that was my phone. Look at that! Only been away a week and they're asking my advice already. No peace for the pious!'

You Have One New Message *Indie Codanda*

'You have one new message,' her phone beeped. At midnight?

She sat up, puzzled; her friends usually didn't message this late, knowing she slept early.

'I want to ravage you,' it said. The number unknown.

'Who are you?' she messaged in return, concern and fear coursing through her.

'The man who knows you wear satin camisoles to bed,' the reply lit up her screen.

Quite afraid now, she picked up the phone to dial for help when it began to ring: the same number.

She answered, in apprehension, only to hear his voice, softly menacing from somewhere within the room . . .

Zend *Anne Green*

A tree falls. A single hand claps. A star implodes. No-one hears but Bodhidharma. He denies it. It is said he stared at a wall for several years. No conclusion was reached. Or wall consulted. Schrödinger was impressed. His cat less so. Unobserved, it slipped away. Or did it?

Z-End *Jenni Doherty*

Once upon a time, Grimmsville stud Ciderfella asked spinster Boldilocks to marry him. She said no; she was too in love with Ms Muffet and busy with their little PC Peep Show, *The Ugly Chuckling*.

Ciderfella was speechless, secretly wishing that some Prince Charming would come instead. It was then that they could all live equally ever after and enjoy the beginning . . .

Biographies of Authors

Moses Abukutsa (Kenya)

Twenty-three-year-old Moses lives in Kakamega and is studying English at a local university. He has had some of his poems published in the *Saturday Standard*, the second largest daily newspaper in Kenya. He loves writing and is a member of the EditRed online writing community.

Sabrina Fatma Ahmad (Bangladesh)

Sabrina, 24, is currently in her senior year at the Independent University, Bangladesh, majoring in Media and Communication Studies. A feature writer for her local newspaper the *Daily Star*, Sabrina has also had work published in an anthology, *Maps and Metaphors*. Website: http://mistress-of-legends.blogspot.com; Email: sabera.jade@gmail.com

Darren Anderson (Northern Ireland/Scotland)

An Irish writer based in Edinburgh, Darren is co-editor of the litzine *Dogmatika* and edits *Laika Poetry Review*. He also writes for *3am* magazine, *Bookmunch* and with the *Brutalist* movement. His fiction recently appeared in *The Flash* anthology alongside Damon Galgut, Rick Moody, Willy Vlautlin and a host of others. Website: www.dogmatika.com

Shonali Bhattacharya (India)

Shonali, 30, from Kolkata, West Bengal, has an MBA in Marketing and runs her father's business of non-ferrous metal alloy castings. She is interested in the socio-cultural diversification of India, bio-diversification, and urban water management. She speaks Bengali, a regional language in India, yet writes in English. This is her first time in print. Email: wiwtstosom@gmail.com

Annie Bien (Hong Kong/North America)

Born in Hong Kong, Annie, 52, lives in New York City. She has poems published, or yet to appear, in *Quattrocento, Snakeskin, Lily, Loch Raven Review, Andwerve, Worm, Centrifugal Eye* and *Miller's Pond*. Also a Pushcart nominee, she made the shortlists in the *Georgetown*

Review Contest 2006, the UK *Guardian* Poetry Workshop and the Strokestown 2007 International Poetry Competition (Ireland). Email: abien@verizon.net

Colin Biggs (Wales)

Growing up in South Wales in a family respectful of the world of literature created a strong desire in Colin to write – especially as worldwide travel and professional advancement have broadened his horizons. He chose his online name *Seventh Age* to reflect the subtle life transition of one on the run-up (down?) to his 49th birthday (although not so subtle in this case as it was accompanied by the birth of a new daughter!) This is his first time in print. Email: colinjohor@hotmail.com

Nathalie Boisard-Beudin (France/Italy)

French by birth, Nathalie currently resides in Rome, Italy. A middle-aged, in-house lawyer working for the European Space Agency, she alleviates her work-related stress by compulsive writing, photography and cooking. Website: http://spacedlaw.blogspot.com; Email: spacedlawyer@yahoo.fr

Mark Buchanan (England)

Mark is a 45-year-old software developer from North London and has been writing short stories and poetry for three years but has had a lifelong interest in literature. He spent his early childhood in Killiney, County Dublin, then lived in Hampshire and Suffolk before moving to London in 1980 to study electronics. This is his first time in print. Email: mb015d0834@blueyonder.co.uk

Hazel Buckingham (England)

Hazel lives with four other people in a house in a town outside London. She kept her words to herself for 44 years, but having released them over the course of the last three years, it appears some people like them. She has had poems and a short story published. When she is not at her keyboard, she can be found in her garden talking to stag beetles and plants. Website: www.myworks.co.uk

Shirley Bunyan (England)

As a child, Shirley took to writing like a duck to water, but a busy lifestyle rendered her writing aspirations dormant for many years. She rediscovered her voice just three years ago, aged 51, after stumbling upon the BBC Get Writing website. Publishing credits include *Poetry Now* and the BBC's *Get Writing Anthology 2004*. Email: bunnybobbins@yahoo.co.uk

Mark Burns (Northern Ireland)

Mark was born in Derry in 1969 and is eternally grateful that he is a child of the sixties. He has contributed writings on music, arts and other stuff to several newspapers and magazines. He writes because he can't sing. Email: markburns@iolfree.ie

Eileen Burzynska (England)

In her sixties, Eileen now only works if it appeals to her – and if she has the time. She has been a folk singer, publisher, teacher, tour operator, bookshop manager, and a former Warsaw Correspondent for a national newspaper when she was living in Poland – not so much a career path as a series of interesting experiences. She started creative writing as a completely new departure and spends many happy hours on the MoreWriting website. Email: eileen@burzynska.plus.com

Julieann Campbell (Northern Ireland)

Julieann was born in Derry where she still resides. Having nurtured a love of the written word since childhood, she became a reporter for the city's oldest newspaper, the *Derry Journal*, although she prefers writing poetry. She is currently co-editing an anthology of the artistic responses to Bloody Sunday to be published by Guildhall Press in 2008. Email: julieann.campbell@derryjournal.com

Robert Capps (England)

Born in 1954, Robert left school aged 11 after having spent a year in a National Children's Home. For most of his life he has lived on the south coast of England working in the hospitality trade and in transport. He started writing poetry and prose after a 40-year absence when he discovered the BBC h2g2 and Get Writing online communities. Website: www.myspace.com/logicus_tracticus

Richard Chalu (England)

Promoting carbon friendliness *way* before it was trendy, Richard hasn't lived further than 12 miles from the very spot he was born 37 years ago in Norwich. He is often seen masquerading as a Finance Director whilst attempting to complete various meaningless writing projects. Married with oodles of children, Richard may contain traces of nut.

Arthur Chappell (England)

Born in Manchester in 1962, Arthur has a degree in literature and philosophy. He was also brainwashed into a cult, which he escaped from in 1985, and writes to prove that he is more than just a victim. He has had several articles, poems and stories published and is a member of the Sealed Knot English Civil War Re-enactment Society. Website: www.arthurchappell.clara.net/contents.htm; Email: arthur@chappell7300.freeserve.co.uk

Andrew Clark (England)

Andrew is 27 and originally from Bromley, Kent. He spent eight years living in Oxford, studying first for a Chemistry degree and then for a doctorate (in a particularly obscure area of Chemical Physics). In 2006, he returned to London to start work as a trainee patent agent and escaped academia before it was too late. He has been writing short stories for around four years, several of which have been published online or in small presses. Email: apclarkwriter@googlemail.com

Indie Codanda (India)

Indie, 36, is a dreamer by aspiration. More worldly requirements, however, mean that she spends her days as an Innovation Consultant instead. Living in Bangalore, India, and travelling a lot, Indie uses her spare time to read, write, dance and sing off-key. Her only quest is to figure out the meaning of life – a puzzle she is no closer to solving after so many years. This is her first time in print. Email: indiewoman@gmail.com

Kevin Connolly (Northern Ireland)

Born in Lancashire in 1961, Kevin moved to Northern Ireland when aged ten. He has various poems and short stories published and has just finished his first novel. Former editor of a food and beverages magazine, he now works in accounts while his liver recovers from all the free booze. Always modest, Kevin thinks he is 'probably the world's best living writer.' Email: stinkalloy@btinternet.com

Gavin Damerell (England)

Aged 30, Gavin lives in Portsmouth, where he was also born. He has a daughter named Leah and at present is earning a living as a postman in the small town of Waterlooville. He has had a number of short stories and poems published in the small presses, and is currently researching material for a children's novel.

Teri Davis-Rouvelas (North America)

Teri lives in Rhode Island and is a member of the Turtle Mountain Band of Ojibwe, North Dakota. She's the proud mother of two grown children along with several different animals. Her work appears in the short story anthology, *Small Voices, Big Confessions*, where she also won the 2006 EditRed Editor's Choice Award. She's currently attempting to learn Spanish without alienating an entire culture or causing an international incident. Email: teri.davisrouvelas@gmail.com

Lynda Day Martin (North America)

Lynda lives in a tiny town in Vermont, USA, with her husband and two cats. She works as an administrative assistant and receptionist at a software company. She writes poetry and makes feverish and intermittent forays into short fiction. She has not been published outside of the MoreWriting website, which has taught her whatever she knows about writing and provides her with staunch companionship in the wee small hours.

Jenni Doherty (Republic of Ireland)

Donegal-born, Jenni's background ranges from publishing, book selling, the public library service, journalism, facilitating creative writing workshops plus organising arts events. Co-author of *That Land Beyond* (2003), Jenni also compiled *Eve… a celebration of creative women* (2006) with Guildhall Press. She is part of the poetry performance group, The Poetry Chicks, has toured the literary festival scene in Australia (2006) and has been widely published in many disciplines. Website: www.myspace.com/irishpenjen; Email: irishpenjen@yahoo.co.uk

Corey Evans (Canada/France)

Formerly an internet development professional, Corey is a graduate of the University of Calgary with a degree in English literature. Having published poetry in popular journals, he lives with his wife and two children in the French Alps where he is at work on his first novel. Website: www.in2orbit.net; Email: corey@in2orbit.net

Roy Everitt (England)

Originally from Essex, Roy now lives in Suffolk. He spent the best part of 30 years as a public servant, 'mostly wishing I could do something else!' Now aged 50, he's a professional copywriter and this is his first prose work in print. Website: www.wellversed.co.uk; Email: roy@wellversed.co.uk

Jo Fajer (Kuwait/China)

Born in 1988 in Kuwait, Jo was raised by her traditional Kuwaiti family until she graduated high school and received a full scholarship to a fine arts school in Dubai. At 19, she dropped out of college to run away to China where she currently lives as a photographer and English teacher. She has never been published. Email: jo.fajer@gmail.com

Ali Froud (England)

Ali lives in Kent and is a wife, mother, gran and a fairly eccentric, dyed-in-the-wool hippy! Her house is full of laughter and music and many, many books. She has been writing poetry for years and branched out into short stories when she joined the BBC Get Writing site back in 2003. Email: spiderbaby48@yahoo.co.uk

Liz Gallagher (Ireland/Spain)

Liz is from Donegal but now lives in the Canary Islands. She is an English Language Teacher and has had poetry and fiction published, or forthcoming, in *Stirring, The Pedestal* magazine, *Wicked Alice, Kaleidowhirl, The Hiss Quarterly, Noö, Word Riot* and *The Mad Hatter's Review* and others. She placed first in the USA-based InterBoard

Poetry Competition in December 2006 and had work published in the Guildhall Press publication, *Eve* (2006). Website: http://agcaint. blogspot.com; Email: isabellavalido@yahoo.es

Anne Green (Northern Ireland)

Anne is a native of Derry but has travelled widely in her search for inspiration, adventure and a chilled glass of Chateau Rieussec 1999 by an infinity pool enjoying panoramic views of Cannes at sunset. Oh, and she writes, too!

Perry Gretton (Australia)

Perry Gretton, 65, lives on the beautiful Central Coast of New South Wales, Australia. While he has written technical material and many articles, he has only recently started on fiction and is currently working on his first novel. Website: www.perrorist.com; Email: perry@perisys.com

Miriam Heinbuch (Germany)

Born in Germany in 1981, Miriam spent ten years in Norway and has worked in theatre and studied English Literature. She now lives in Berlin and writes reviews for www.madgoth.de. Website: www. myspace.com/nephilia81; Email: nephilia81@gmx.net

Lee Henderson (Australia)

Lee is a Landscaping and Earthmoving contractor: 'I dig holes, I fill 'em in, I build rockwalls. I write poetry and tiny little stories and have had a few published in ezines. I'm also an Australian who lives in the country a fair way from the big smoke.'

Clarissa Henry (Austria/England)

Born in London, Clarissa describes herself as a 'polyglot cosmopolitan, Jill of all trades, mistress of none.' She has worked in London, Berlin and Paris and has taught Business English at the University of Paris XII. A former documentary filmmaker and author, Clarissa now works in Vienna with a music-publishing house and is 'waiting for fate to take me by the hand again.'

Azfarul Islam (Bangladesh)

'For me, Azfarul Islam (aka Le Chupacabra), composing a plot in sixty words is unheard of. I joined the *Rising Stars* magazine in Bangladesh a few years ago and established myself with anime and video game reviews, and more relevantly, fiction verging towards prolixity. While the quality is for the readers to judge, I thoroughly enjoyed writing them. Now aged nineteen, I occupy myself with cooking, music (I love my bass guitar), art (ie doodling), anime, video games and football . . . oh, yeah, and studies.'

Karen Jones (Scotland)

A full-time mother and carer, Karen writes – in as much spare time as she has – short stories, novels, comedy and occasionally poetry. She has been published in *Writers' Forum* magazine, *Candis* magazine, Writers' Bureau website and reached the initial short list for the Asham Award 2007.

Lynda Kenny (Northern Ireland)

Mother to three teenagers and living in Newry, County Down, Lynda rarely finds time for herself. When she does, she is an enthusiastic amateur poker player and likes to read and write. Lynda was first published in the Guildhall Press anthology *Eve... a celebration of creative women* in 2006 with a few of her other micro-stories. Email: lyndabken@aol.com

Rachiel Key (Philippines)

Half-Filipino, half-Chinese, 26-year-old Rachiel was born and raised in Manila. She graduated with a degree in Journalism and is currently working in Dubai as an executive secretary for Al-Futtaim Carillion, one of the major construction companies in UAE. This is the first time Rachiel has published her works for an international market. Email: rachiel_key@hotmail.com

Estelle Kirk (England)

Brought up near Liverpool, Estelle spent most of her working life in London and now resides in Wycombe. Past roles have included barmaid, student, textile designer, lone traveller, hopeful romantic, competitive rower, designer of greetings cards, waitress, cleaner, library assistant, care worker, gardener, overworked teacher and, most importantly, mother. 'I long for those quiet midnight hours,

when everyone else is asleep, to carve a story out of words.' Email:
fatgardener@hotmail.co.uk

Heidrun Knikander (Germany/Finland)

Born in Germany in 1960, Heidrun now resides in Finland and
undertakes North American Studies at the University of Helsinki.
Married with three children, she began writing after the birth of
her first child. She has a Master's degree in Forestry and writes scientific articles, publishing her first book on Environmental History,
*Der nordamerikanische Bison und das Grasland (The North American
Bison and The Grassland)*, with Die Blau Eule, 2003.

Anatoly Kudryavitsky (Russia/Ireland)

Born in 1954 in Moscow with Irish/Russian nationality, Anatoly
now lives in Dublin and works as a teacher/literary translator. He
has published seven poetry collections in Russia and two in Ireland,
with Goldsmith Press and Doghouse Books, plus an anthology of
Russian poetry in English translation, *A Night in the Nabokov Hotel*
(Dedalus). Website: http://uk.geocities.com/akudryavitsky

NE Tab Loid (Terra Firma)

This author wishes to remain anonymous for reasons unstated but
which we respect.

Calvin Lord (England)

Calvin, 43, lives in Bolton, Lancashire. He's been writing for three
years, but not too seriously, as he has a demanding career as a director of a business in North West England which demands exten-
sive travelling, particularly in China. He is coming to the end of an
important long-term project and once this is completed, he plans
to take some time off and finish his first novel. Email: calvinlord2@
hotmail.com

Elizabeth Madden (Scotland/England)

A native of Scotland now living in Southern England, Elizabeth is
a former teacher of English Literature and Theatre Studies. She
writes poetry, plays and short stories and is working on her first
novel. She has been published in the *Slingink Shorts Anthology* and
Zoetrope magazine. Website: www.myspace.com/lyubaranevskya

Amanda Mair (Northern Ireland)

Born in Northern Ireland, Amanda lived for several years in North Scotland before returning to this beautiful island. She has two children and three grandchildren and is a civil servant manager in the DOE Planning Service. Her interests include active involvement in her local church, reading and writing. She mostly writes for herself and has had a few pieces published in the Banbridge Writers' Circle booklet *Homefront Memories* in 2006.

Felicity McCall (Northern Ireland)

Felicity was born in South Armagh in 1957. She worked for 20 years as a media news journalist. Now living in North West Ireland, with a teenage daughter, she is a freelance writer, arts facilitator, filmmaker and actor. Publishing and performance credits include five books (one online), contributions to anthologies, including *Eve... a celebration of creative women* (Guildhall Press, 2006) and three plays. She has also written and published the screenplay of *Agnes Jones* and her new novel, *Finding Lauren*, will be published by Guildhall Press in 2007. She is Ireland officer for the miscarriage of justice group, Portia. Website: www.inspiricom.net/felicitymccall; Email: felicitymccall@hotmail.com

Fionnuala McGowan (Northern Ireland)

Her career as a dedicated social worker converts the currency to crumbs, apposite and advantageous as Fionnuala has taken to writing like an Anatidae to aqua. A veteran of *Eve*, and survivor of the après jamboree, she is nudging fame as her skills sharpen. The clock is ticking ...

Gary McMahon (England)

Gary, 47, a postman no more, has a fistful of degrees and diplomas but no money. He was hoping there would be money in collaborating with the enemy, but this turned out not to be the case. His book, *Camp In Literature,* was published in 2006 (North Carolina: McFarland). He writes occasional film articles – see *Sight and Sound* magazine – and is currently working on a book about Kurt Vonnegut. He also tends to decline party invites. Website: www. myspace.com/authorgary

Tamzin Mole (England)

Tamzin has been writing for fun since the age of seven when she was given an ancient Spanish typewriter with an upside-down exclamation mark (¡). She has since upgraded to a laptop and now works mainly on short stories. She is 38, lives in the south of England with her partner, and has learnt not to use exclamation marks! (Except in dire emergencies.)

Maxwell Mutami (Zimbabwe)

Aged 33 and currently based in Harare, Maxwell has had several poems and short stories published in hard print and online magazines. His poetry collection, *When The Dust Has Settled,* was published in New York in August 2006 and is available from several online bookstores. Website: www.editred.com/mmutami; Email: vamutami@yahoo.com

Julie Okon (Poland/England)

Julie has been living in the suburbs of Warsaw for the past 14 years and has a 20-year-old son and a 14-year-old daughter. She also has what is rather amusingly called an 'estranged' Polish husband, a deaf Dalmatian dog, and a feral cat. She has been writing for herself since school: 'I suppose a blank piece of paper has always been a passive, non-threatening receptacle on which to spill the beans.' She has had some poems published before and is a member of the MoreWriting site www.morewriting.co.uk

Neil Outram (England)

Born in Essex in 1980, Neil is self-employed, studies psychology, and plans to study English Literature with creative writing. Writing is his first love, which he does in a variety of forms: short fiction, play scripts and short-film scripts. He also enjoys photography, filmmaking, acting and voice work. He has had three poems published in book anthologies and a parody article published in a magazine. His main aim is to have his plays produced. Email: n.outram@blueyonder.co.uk

Jill Paiton (Australia/England)

Originally from York, Jill moved to Australia when aged seven. Now in her forties, she lives with her artist husband in coastal Victoria where they keep Cashmere goats, ducks, chickens, three cats and a very spoilt Springer spaniel. She is a qualified Community Welfare Worker, currently employed in adult education assisting people with disabilities. Jill enjoys writing topical, social-comment vignettes with a twist in the tail. This is her first time in print. Email: serrindip-pidydog@yahoo.com.au

Gavin Parish (England)

Gavin Parish is a 30-year-old civil servant living in London and – disregarding 15 minutes of fame on the Radio Kent website – this is his first time in print. He entertains thoughts of script writing for the Beeb (*Doctors, Doctor Who*, anything with *Doctor* in the title) and reckons a bit of conciseness might keep those execs awake at the story-pitching stage. Email: gavin.parish@btinternet.com

Nicky Philips (England)

Born in Broxbourne in 1955, Nicky's love of language developed at Ware Grammar School from where she went on to become a multilingual secretary in the music-publishing industry before working at Canada House overlooking Trafalgar Square. Now self-employed, she writes whenever possible and has had several pieces published. Nicky lives in a Hertfordshire village with her husband, teenage daughters and dog.

Alexander Prophet (Barbados/Germany)

Born in Barbados in 1968, Alexander co-hosted a local radio show, *The People Tomorrow*, as a teenager and went on to become a freelance writer for local newspapers. He then spent three years travelling, mostly across the USA and Europe, before eventually settling in Frankfurt am Main, Germany. In 1998, he became actively involved in the music industry as a promoter, music critic, and press agent for diverse music promoters, artists and art galleries. He's been living in Berlin since 1999.

Dan Purdue (England)

Dan Purdue is 30, lives in Warwickshire, and works as a design engineer for a medical company. He started writing fiction three years ago and began work on a sci-fi novel at the beginning of 2007. His 50-word story, *Brave Jack*, was a runner-up in London website

Spread the Word's *microSTORY* competition in 2006, but this will be the first time his writing has made it into print.

Amy Rafferty (Scotland)

Amy is a writer and musician who lives in Glasgow with her two young sons. She writes both poetry and prose and has been published by *Waste Notes Fiction* and *Fire Opal*. She sings with cult band The Recovery Club and collaborates with many other local artists, writers and musicians. Website: www.myspace.com/amyschwamy; Email: amypaloma@hotmail.com

Anne Rainbow (England)

Anne splits her time between homes in Surrey and Devon. Fast approaching 60, Anne's career included IT consultancy, Maths/IT teaching and authoring/editing IT and Maths textbooks. Recently, she created RedPen – an online workshop for writers to hone their editing skills – on the MoreWriting website. Several of her poems appear in anthologies and many can be seen on her poem-a-day blog, but this is Anne's first foray into short-story writing. Website: http://blog. annerainbow.me.uk; Email: anne.rainbow@btinternet.com

Kitty Redding (England)

Kitty Redding is 36 years old and is the proud parent of three children, all of whom have inherited her love of reading and the theatre. She lives in the English Midlands and is a School Project Manager for Worldwide Volunteering. She has been writing short stories, plays and screenplays for about four years. She has had some stories published online, a play performed by 50 school children and a short film being produced. She is currently writing her first novel. Email: kitty@kittyred.co.uk

Stephen Reilly (Northern Ireland/Wales)

Brought up in Northern Ireland, Stephen left home aged 18, read Modern and Mediaeval Languages at Jesus College, Cambridge, and qualified as a Chartered Accountant after living in France for two years. Following a career in finance, ultimately becoming Finance Director of a UK utility, he has retired early, aged 47, and currently lives in Wales. Website: www.linguapura.com; Email: shreilly@linguapura.com

Carolyn Roberts (Scotland)

Carolyn grew up in Edinburgh and has lived in Glasgow for the last 13 years. She is 30 years old and works for a mental health charity. Carolyn has been writing for most of her life and has previously published some poetry and magazine articles. She likes to think she enjoys writing 60-worders because they demand writing discipline but suspects it is really more to do with laziness. Website: www.kimire.com

Sam Robinson (New Zealand/East Timor)

Sam, 55, a New Zealander currently resident in Timor-Leste, is an accountant by training who has worked as an international banking advisor in South East Asia for the past 15 years. He has written a biography which was published in 1993. He speaks Indonesian and smatterings of other languages, and lists creative writing, compulsive book buying, genealogy, opera and tennis amongst his hobbies. All but the last of these have been significantly influenced by this publication. Email: sam@thewoolstore.co.nz

Steven Schusman (England)

Steven is a previously unpublished 40-something family man who deals in collectables. He lives just North of London and writes in fits and starts, generally whilst sober, but with more interesting results when not. He loves the sound of pelting rain and the silence of falling snow, especially when he's indoors and traffic wardens are out on duty. His interests include observing eccentrics, psychology, cricket and stand-up comedy.

Nina Simon (England)

Nina is a Londoner in her forties and works for her local school library service. Much of her spare time is spent reading children's fiction. Married with two teenage daughters, Nina has been writing for about two years. Initially, she only wrote poetry but tried prose when she read a story she was sure she could write better. This is her first time in print.

Christopher Spalding (England)

Christopher is a 39-year-old actor now resident in Bury St Edmunds. Originally from Essex, he first trod the boards at Colchester's

Mercury Theatre at the tender age of 16. Chris decided to turn his hand to writing to fill the gaps between parts and is currently enrolled on a creative writing course. This is his first published piece of work. Website: www.karzy.co.uk

Sarah Star (England)

Sarah Star lives between Sandhurst Military Academy and Broadmoor Hospital for the Criminally Insane, but thankfully has nothing to do with either institution. She has just turned 40 so is at her peak, and despite several better jobs, now keeps office for her dad's business. She has been shortlisted for several competitions and has had several stories published online. Currently, she is working on her first novel with her agent, Clare Conville.

Petya Mihaylova Stefanova-Gieridis (Bulgaria)

Born in 1975 in Targovishte where she still lives and works, Petya has a degree in Bulgarian and English from The University of Plovdiv. A teacher of English and translator, Petya has published works online with www.liternet.bg and www.studiohousepro.co.uk; Email: petya_gleridis@yahoo.com

Teresa Stenson (England)

Teresa serves lattés to pay the bills, daydreaming as she froths the milk. Her stories have appeared in anthologies from Leaf Books and Earlyworks Press, and in publications from hum-drum and *The Orphan Leaf Review*. She is 26 and resides in York, where she is currently working on a short film with hum-drum Films. Email: treacle_tree_2000@yahoo.com

Roy Weltman (Zimbabwe/Israel)

Roy was born in Rhodesia/Zimbabwe in 1965. Growing up in apartheid South Africa, he felt the pains of human destruction and wrote to understand that pain. Roy's genres are predominantly poetry and short stories. With careers in insurance, real estate and high tech, he finally settled down to his dream – breeding horses. Roy lives in Israel and has two children. Email: royweltman@yahoo.com

Darren Wheatley (England)

Hailing from the historic lace-making village of Long Eaton, Derbyshire, Darren wrote initially as an outlet for the voices in his head. Now the voices are all that are left. Then they invented word processors and all of a sudden all those grubby notebooks seemed irrelevant. The words continued to flow. Eventually, someone figured out a way to squirt these words around the world in an instant, and so Darren became published at last. Conforming nicely to his short attention span, poems and micro-stories became his chosen outlet. Email: weaver2go@yahoo.co.uk

Maureen Wilkinson (England)

Belfast-born Maureen resides in Norfolk. Since retiring in 2006 and taking up writing as a hobby, she has had about 40 short stories published in various magazines all over the world. She has been told she has a warped sense of humour. She says that's because she likes to hang naked by her toes in a tree and frighten the motorists. Email: littlewhitewolf@gmail.com

Writers' Websites

Below are some of the main UK-based writers' webites on which most of the *Wonderful World of Worders* authors first published their work. Some of the site descriptions are courtesy of the relevant Site Directors.

BBC Get Writing

The former national BBC Get Writing website still boasts great online resources that include: creative writing mini-courses; archive reading material; tools and quizzes; writing-craft articles; watch-and-listen literary events; general arts information; drama; radio and "writersroom" for television scripts. The interactive community, live chat forums and personalised members portfolios were terminated in March 2005. Active web links: www.bbc.co.uk/dna/getwriting/links; www.bbc.co.uk/northernireland/learning/getwritingni

EditRED

EditRED is a lively writing community that enables writers to develop existing work, break into publishing, promote existing published work and sell more books if they have them. EditRED.com was designed by writers with one user in mind: the WRITER. What we have created is a site that writers of all levels can grow from. Whether you are starting out and need insightful critiques, are looking for the best journals to submit to or have books that you want to promote and sell, the features and structure of EditRED will enable you to do all of this with more success and in a fun environment. Websites: www.editred.com; www.myspace.com/short_stories

MoreWriting

MoreWriting is a free site where you can hone your writing skills whether interested in creating fiction, poetry, comedy or factual works. You can even add sound tracks and images. Build on your strengths and tackle your weaknesses by seeing what other writers think of your ideas and style. Build up a portfolio of reviewed works; earn money through publication; discuss technical matters or simply have fun playing word games to spark creativity. A number of the Worders included in this book were authored and polished by site members during friendly competitions on MoreWriting. You'll find a warm welcome if you'd like to join us. Dr Gordon Brooks, Site Director. Website: www.morewriting.co.uk

MySpace

MySpace is a social place for friends where members share photographs, journal entries/blogs, music and interests with a growing network of people worldwide. Creating a profile is fast and easy. You can disclose as much or as little information about yourself as you want. MySpace will always keep your personal information private and confidential. Website: www.myspace.com

Writers' Dock

Writers' Dock caters for all genres of writing. It has a vibrant community of aspiring writers: amateur and professional authors, scriptwriters, poets, songwriters and journalists – published or unpublished – all supporting each other with every aspect of writing, be it spelling and grammar through to dealing with success or failure. Writers' Dock has daily activities, groups, chat rooms, podcasts, writing aids, celebrity guests, a great social atmosphere and lots more. Everybody is welcome to get involved, whether you are completely new to these creative processes or an accomplished expert. Stephen Gritton, Site Director. Website: www.writersdock.org

Index